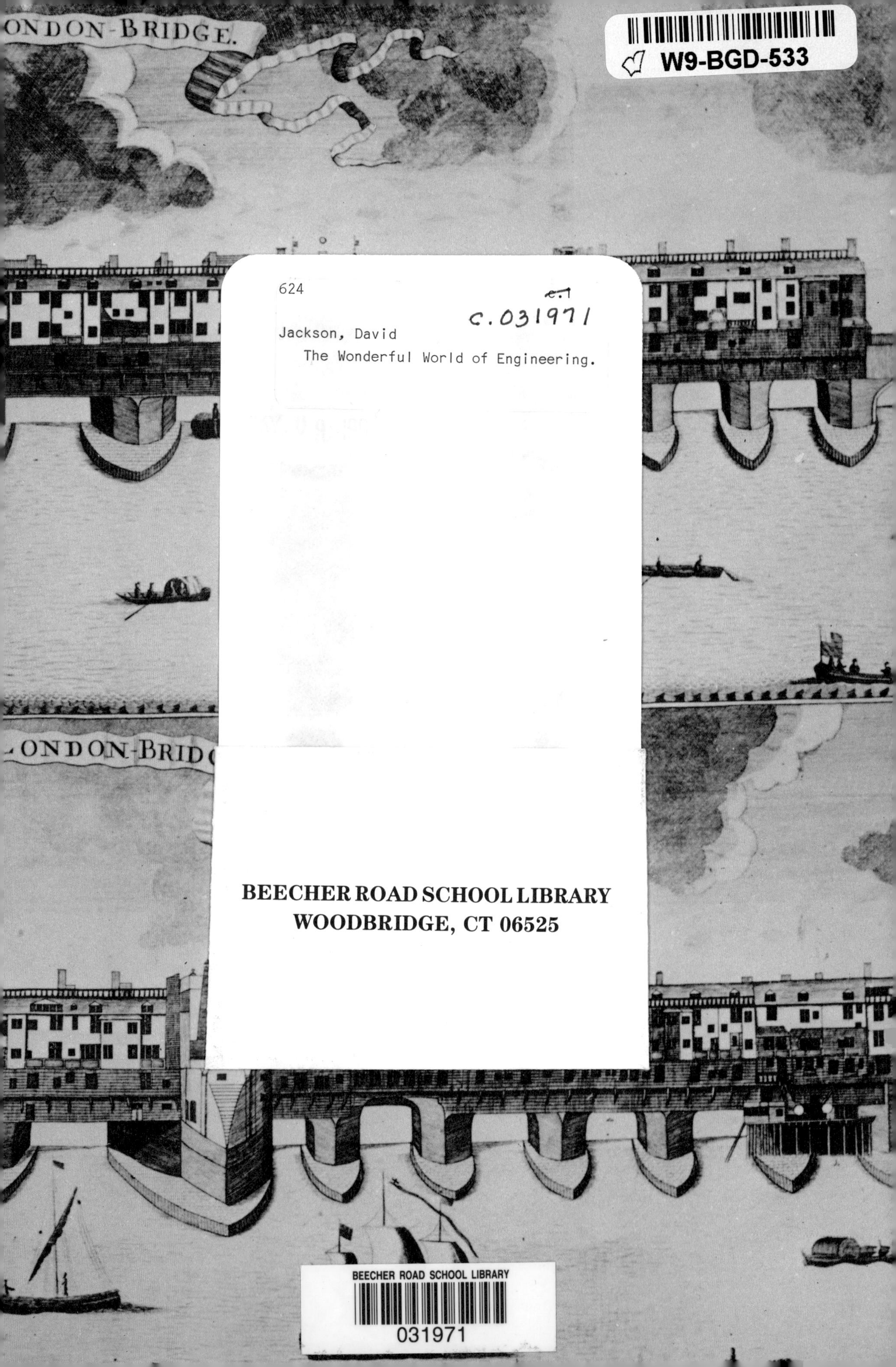
ONDON-BRIDGE.
LONDON-BRID

The Wonderful World of Engineering

Dam at Watts Bar, on the Tenessee River.

The Wonderful World of Engineering

David Jackson

Doubleday and Company Inc.

Garden City, New York

Library of Congress Catalog Card Number 69-10009

Printed in Yugoslavia

Contents

page

Certain words and phrases in this book are followed by the symbol☞. Whenever you see this symbol it means that you can look up the word or phrase in the alphabetical glossary at the end of the book and find more information or a fuller definition of the term.

1 Why Man Builds

In his never-ending struggle to tame nature, man has been driven by four basic needs: agriculture, building, communications, and power. The practical art and science of civil engineering☞ arose and grew to meet these needs.

When primitive men gave up their life of wandering, they became tillers of fields, settling in small communities. To find shelter from the weather and storage for his harvest, man became a builder. In the course of time, different settlements came to depend on each other for the exchange of goods. And so there had to be links between settlements to provide passage for men and materials. Eventually, men learned to harness the power of nature to relieve them of some of the arduous tasks of everyday life.

Agriculture gave rise to hydraulic engineering, which developed from the irrigation☞ basins and canals☞ of ancient peoples, from their transient reclamation☞ works to the vast irrigation and reclamation projects of today. Building gave rise to structural engineering, which developed from the monumental architecture of Egypt, Greece, and Rome, to the great framed structures of today. Communications gave rise to the widest variety of civil engineering works. From the earliest times man has used tracks, mountain passes, rivers and sea for transport, and now, in the 20th century he also uses the air. As his civilization became more intricate, so the need for safe and speedy passage for himself and his material goods began to grow. In time, his tracks developed from the jungle path to the paved Roman road, and to the great concrete☞ highways of today.

Power was first derived from the ox trudging in a circle, and man treading a wheel, from primitive capstan and rope pulley block; then from the windmill, and finally from today's water turbine at the foot of a massive dam. As world population increases, so the provision of adequate water and power supplies grows more urgent.

Building a cathedral, from a 15th-century miniature by Jehan Forquet.

2 From Wasteland to Farmland

Four thousand years ago, Queen Semiramis ruled over the Assyrians. On her tomb was inscribed: "I constrained the mighty river to flow according to my will and led its water to fertilize lands that before had been barren and without inhabitants." A thousand years before that, the first pharaoh, King Menes, had introduced a system of basin irrigation☞ along the Nile, which, with some improvements, still plays its part in Egyptian agriculture today. From China, Egypt, India, and Iraq, irrigation spread westward. When the Spaniards arrived in Mexico and Peru they found man-made water supply systems which the Indians had been using for centuries.

On the whole, nature has given man an ample and dependable supply of water. It is a resource unchanged by time: falling as rain, it flows to the sea, then returns to the clouds, in an endless cycle. But its distribution on the earth varies enormously, and in general there is either too little or too much of it.

More than three quarters of the world's land has insufficient natural water for agriculture, and therefore requires irrigation. Some places have to be irrigated for part of the year only. Where there is too much water, the land must be drained. And so men call upon the civil engineer to drain and reclaim the marshes and the lowlands. They ask him to bring water to the deserts and dry lands, and to store surplus water in the wet seasons for use in the dry seasons. To do this the engineer must alter and regulate great rivers, raise embankments☞, dams, and barrages☞, construct aqueducts☞ and sluices☞, build vast reservoirs, and fashion many thousands of miles of canals☞ and channels of every description.

Egypt's Nile Basin is a modern example of river control and irrigation on the grand scale. The Nile is a unique river that flows through waterless desert for most of its total length of nearly 3000 miles. The lives of thousands of people depend on the volume and regularity of its annual

Desilting works at Imperial Dam on the Colorado River.

flood, brought down from its mountain sources. Over many centuries, the Egyptians evolved the technique of basin irrigation, which means trapping part of the annual floodwaters within low earth embankments built beside the river. The Nile usually overflowed at the right time of year for planting crops. If the waters arrived early or late, if they were much lower or higher than normal, then famine or flood threatened. We may recall the seven lean years of the Biblical pharaoh's dream.

The original Aswan Dam was the first of the great modern dams that have been built in increasing numbers in the 20th century. It lies in a granite gorge where the First Cataract runs near the town of Aswan. It was begun in 1898 and, with the labor of thousands of workmen, it was completed in 1902, after three and a half years of work. Its bold design and famous site have given it a prominent place among the world's great engineering structures. That the reservoir should submerge ancient monuments, the exquisite Temple of Philae among them, was unavoidable. Thus at times the past must give way to the present.

The engineers had undertaken to throw a massive wall of granite, $1\frac{1}{4}$ miles long and containing 180 sluices, across a river that in flood would thrust more than 4 million tons of water an hour against them. The sluices allow the Nile flood to pass freely, so that the load of silt☞ is carried on down river. When the flood is subsiding and the danger of silting up the reservoir is reduced, the gates are partly closed and, although most of the water passes on into the river, enough is held back to fill the great reservoir.

The Aswan Dam, its associated diversion barrage at Assuit, 400 miles downstream, and the great system of irrigation canals, brought immense benefits to Egypt. No longer did the farmer have to wait for the annual flood, no longer did he fear its vagaries. At any time of the year, within certain limits, water could be directed onto his land in controlled quantities. The results were astonishing: within a few years prosperity rose sharply.

The benefits were so great that the Aswan Dam was heightened twice, until the great reservoir held five times as much water as it originally did. But the demand for irrigation water by the growing population of Egypt was insatiable. Farmers and engineers alike looked longingly at the floodwater running to waste through the Aswan sluices. Furthermore, growing Egypt demanded power for its industries and homes.

Long-range planners therefore began to think of the answers. Moreover, they were mindful that the reservoirs at Aswan and those higher up the river might not be filled in time of drought; and that unprecedented floods might breach the river banks and destroy the many villages in the Nile Delta. At first, a third heightening of the Aswan Dam was proposed, but in the end the Egyptian Government decided to build an entirely new dam, known as the New High Aswan Dam. Sited

Flood control and irrigation in the Nile Valley. The map shows some of the main dams in the scheme, including the Aswan Dam (a) and the Gezira Dam (b).

four miles to the south of the old dam, it is the last step in the control of the Nile; the old dam is used to produce hydroelectric power☞. The New High Aswan Dam is designed to raise the Nile behind it and to create a top reservoir level 200 feet higher than the present reservoir. It is 3 miles long and 350 feet high, and will hold 130 times as much water as the original 1902 reservoir. Its estimated cost is £500 million, or $1,195,000,000. The new dam has no sluiceways or shipping locks☞. It is a solid impenetrable barrier, and the Nile water on its way to the Egyptian fields passes through, and is controlled in, huge tunnels driven through the rock on both banks.

When this vast scheme is completed and the Nile is brought under final control, some will remember the prophetic words of Winston Churchill who, in 1899, wrote of the day when "nearly every drop of water which drains into the whole valley of the Nile shall be amicably divided among the river people, and the Nile itself shall perish gloriously and never reach the sea."

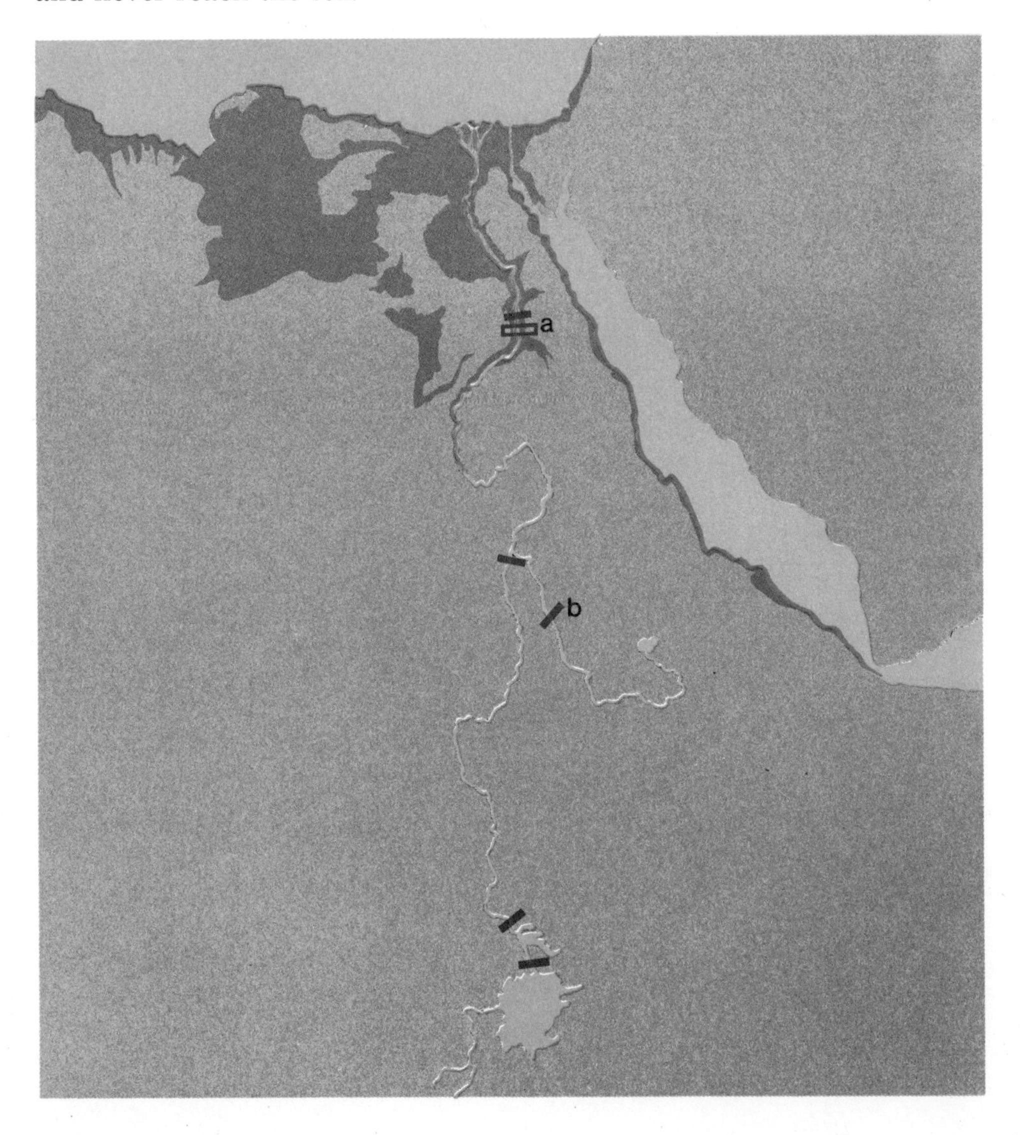

Irrigation dams are designed to store water. The next step in irrigation is to construct a system of canals and channels feeding the land from a natural or man-made source: a river, or a reservoir. When the feeder canals☞ reach the area to be irrigated, they branch out into many smaller channels, which are spread out systematically, and share out the water over the dry land. As the irrigation network gives up more and more of its water, the channels get smaller and smaller.

When the engineer wants to drain land of an excess of water, his aim is just the opposite of irrigation. He digs many small channels, or drains, which collect the excess water from particular areas of the marsh and carry it to the main drainage☞ channel, just as the tributaries of a river flow into the main river. As the drainage network collects more and more water, the main collecting drain gets larger.

There are important differences between the two kinds of network, for irrigation is adjusted to needs, whereas drainage, depending mainly on rainfall, is not subject to man's will. The bed of an irrigation channel is kept as high as possible so that water can flow onto the land; the bed of a drainage channel is kept as low as possible so that excess water flows off the land.

The main drainage canal, carrying all the water it has collected from its tributary channels, empties into a receiving basin, which may be a river, lake, or sea. If the water in this basin is subject to floods or high tides, the engineer must build a check structure at or near the outlet to prevent the floodwater from surging back into the drainage channels. The structure contains gates or sluices that may be closed to prevent back-flow, or opened to allow the drainage canal to empty into the receiving basin.

The Black Bush polder scheme in Guyana is a good example illustrating these principles. It contains irrigation and drainage channels in parallel. The extensive Black Bush swamp was a jungle, subject to alternate flood and drought. Few men had dreamed that this great area could be brought under cultivation, until the pressure of population and the increased demand for land at last turned the engineer's visions into reality.

The engineers had to dig up 9,000,000 cubic yards of earth to form the channels. This, and the hundred and one related jobs that had to be done in dense jungle swamp, put the construction engineers' courage and enterprise to a severe test.

The engineering crews had to beat and hack their way into the undergrowth. There were no roads, no rivers, nothing but marsh and thick jungle. As the draglines☞ excavating the channels churned their way slowly forward, supplies followed in boats, for the newly cut channels immediately filled with the water drained from the swamp. As the crews moved deeper into the interior, they used radio telephones

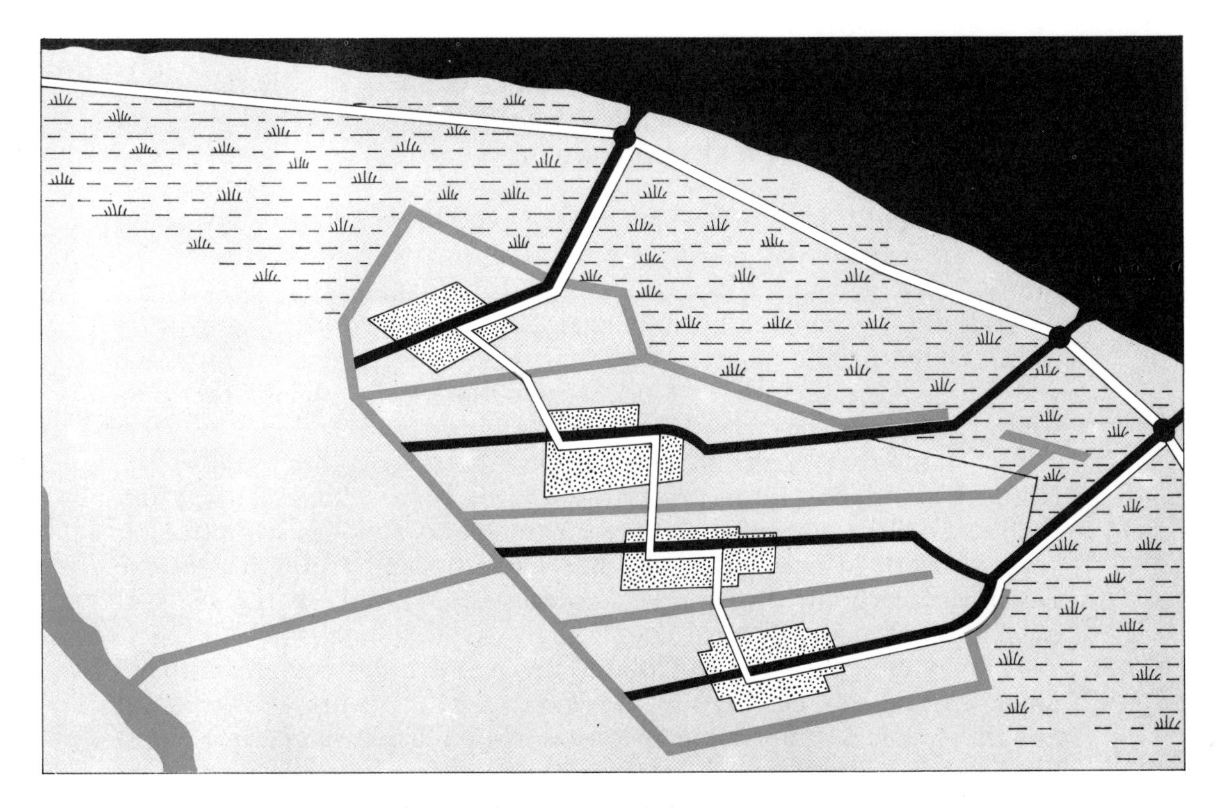

The Black Bush Polder scheme, showing system of drains (black) and irrigation canals (blue). Roads linking new settlements are shown in white.

to keep in touch with the base, and lived on houseboats beside their machines. Proceeding up the great canals that the draglines left behind, the engineers could see the ungainly machines swinging their loaded buckets of earth in great arcs across the sky.

The Black Bush drainage and irrigation scheme is based on a network of channels draining surplus water into the Atlantic Ocean. Large control sluices regulate the flow and keep the water of the ocean back from the land that is below sea level. A network of irrigation channels brings water into the fields; it is controlled by hundreds of sluices of various forms, so that the farmer may get the correct amount of water for his crops. The water is brought from the nearest river, the Canje. Large pumps force the water into a long canal that feeds the smaller channels running through the farmlands. Since the Canje River is at times liable to dry up, it is connected by another long canal with the much larger Berbice River, so that there is always enough water.

Behind the men of the Black Bush swamp project were the engineers who planned and calculated; those who conceived the project; and those who organized and planned the operations. Their next task might be a bridge, a road, a harbor, or a dam in some very different country. But as they moved on to their next job, and to the next after that, they took with them thoughts of the thousands of people settled on the land they had won back from swamp and jungle.

On Holland's great new IJsselmeer dam, there stands a stone on which are carved the words: "A nation that is alive builds for its future."

In all history there has been no example to compare with the struggle of the Dutch people in protecting and reclaiming their land from the sea. The saying goes that "God created the world, except the Low Countries, which were created by the Dutch themselves."

For hundreds of years the Dutch have been struggling against the North Sea without pause, protecting and reclaiming their land. From time to time the sea strikes back with tremendous violence, destroying years of work in a single night. But patiently and triumphantly the Dutch people build up again. They must ever build, or the sea will quickly take back their hard-won land.

The heroes in the story of Holland are many and, for the most part, unknown and unsung. Perhaps the greatest of them are the windmill and the dredger☞. For some 600 years windmills pumped water out of the low-lying country back into the sea. Although electric and diesel pumps have largely replaced them, a few windmills are still in use. For about a hundred years the dredger has been singing its shanty. To the eyes of the civil engineer, the torn bed of sea and river rising in great

The Netherlands in 1900 (left), and today (right). Reclamation projects, finished and planned, are shown in red; red line marks the IJsselmeer Dam.

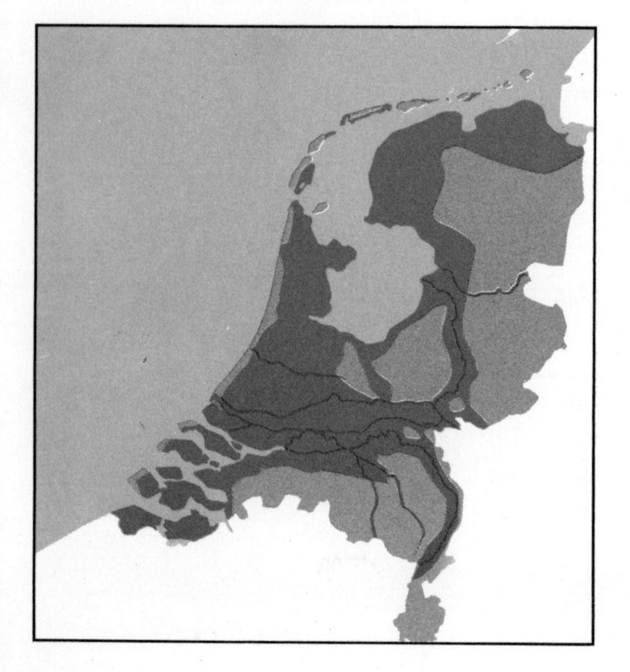

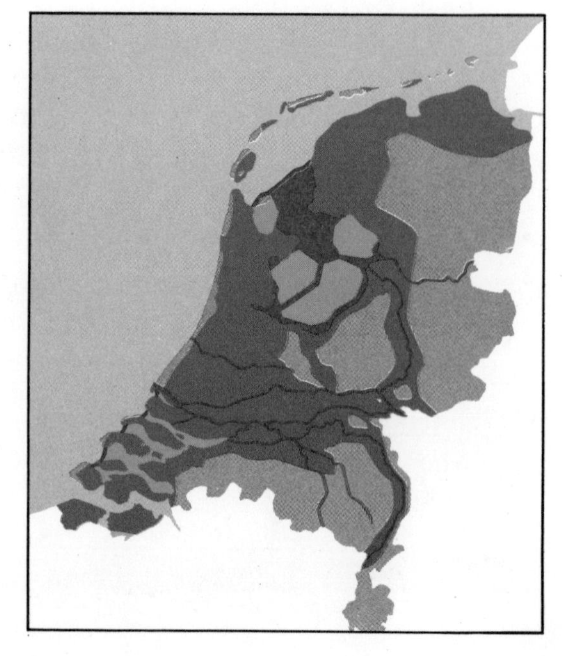

lumps above the waters is the token of his achievement. To his ears, the squelch and splash of the seabed falling into the hopper barges alongside is a chant of victory.

Centuries of war against the sea have made the Dutch the foremost experts on dredging. Their fleets of dredges, barges, pumps, and tugs are by far the largest in the world. To understand why, we must remember that their method of flood protection and land reclamation☞ has always been to construct dikes☞. These are embankments, or dams, of sand and clay usually excavated from the bed of sea, lake, or river. For centuries the excavation was done laboriously by manual labor, and even the first predecessors of the modern dredger were operated manually. With the coming of the steam dredger, and today with the diesel or diesel-electric dredger, dike construction schemes have become much more ambitious; today, engineers devise ever bolder plans as they work out new ways of protecting and reclaiming the land.

New machines give rise to more daring schemes of modern civil engineering☞, but the reclamation of the IJsselmeer is one of the most ambitious engineering projects of mankind. It began about 40 years ago and, even with the use of modern machinery, it will take another 11 years to complete.

The IJsselmeer was a great inland sea, which has been cut off by an enclosing dam 20 miles long across its junction with the North Sea. In enclosing this inland sea, which was some 1300 square miles in area, the coastline of Holland was reduced by 200 miles. The old Dutch saying: "shorten the coast, close the coast," has been fulfilled by this

Workers pile stones onto willow mats, an early stage in the construction of the 20-mile-long barrier dam that shuts off the IJsselmeer from the North Sea.

3 Man Must Build

Early builders were at first concerned almost entirely with constructing shelters against rain, cold, wild beasts, and human foes. Later, as their civilizations developed, they built temples, council chambers, bazaars, and palaces. They took a special delight in erecting pyramids, towers, obelisks, coliseums, and the like.

The story of modern structures is the story of the break from the materials of the past. Great and noble structures were built in brick, timber, and particularly in stone, but now steel and concrete☞ have largely replaced them. With these newer materials we can build to greater heights, span wider gaps, and carry heavier loadings than ever before. In many countries today, mountainous masses of steel and concrete are reaching to the skies on a scale undreamed of in earlier times. Engineers have been able to do this because the rise of the science of structures and the advent of steel and concrete have enabled them to conceive and build their buildings and their structures as frameworks.

Before this, the walls of buildings were "bearing" walls☞: they carried the dead weight and the live load of the structure. The modern large building, however, is essentially a framework or skeleton of steel or concrete that supports the roof and floors. The outside walls are enclosing or "curtain" walls☞, and often their weight at each floor is also taken by the framework. So the "sidewalk superintendent," gaping curiously at the busy scene on a building site, may see the walls rising simultaneously from the ground and midway between roof and ground. Since the walls do not carry the structure, they are sometimes made of glass or plastic.

When the lift-slab☞ method was first devised, some people described it as a way of constructing a building from the top downward. The description, however fanciful, draws attention to the novelty of the system. The method does, nevertheless, give an excellent illustration of the framework principle employed in most modern buildings.

Building the sail-like roofs of the new Opera House, Sydney, Australia.

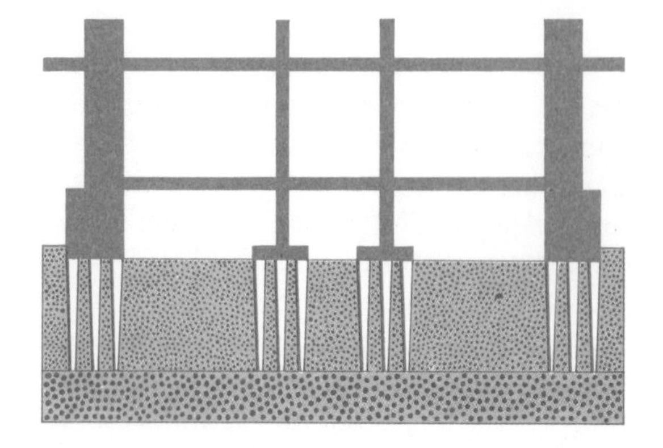

Left, model by Mies van der Rohe for a glass skyscraper, 1920. Right, Tokyo hotel designed by Frank Lloyd Wright; it rests on a concrete raft (diagram).

One begins by constructing the various floors and the roof on top of one another, and around the columns☞, at ground level. These are then lifted by powerful hydraulic jacks☞ to their correct positions in the structure, and permanently connected to the columns. In the case of a nine-storey building, the columns may be erected in three stages, and the tops of each stage temporarily braced together by the ascending roof. As the roof and higher floors move upward, they leave behind lower floors which, secured to the columns, serve to brace them permanently together. In this type of structure, therefore, the floors and the roof serve the added purpose of forming part of the framework. When roof and floors are all finally in place and connected to the columns, the protective walls can be built up from ground level.

In large buildings, the civil engineer's main task is the design of frameworks and foundations☞. Where a building is supported by its walls, the weight is spread out over a large area. This gives relatively low pressures on the ground and makes foundation work easy. But in a modern building framework, the load is carried by a small number of columns, which leads to highly concentrated ground pressure. Hence the foundations must be strong, particularly if the ground is weak.

If the ground is reasonably firm, it is often enough to place the columns on spread footings☞. These are blocks of concrete of such area as to spread the load to within the carrying strength of the ground. On soft ground, a building is sometimes put on a concrete raft, which is a footing covering the whole ground plan area. A building on its raft is virtually floating on the ground beneath. A method often used is to drive a number of piles☞ under each column foundation. The piles are made long enough to rest on the hard ground below the soft surface. The building is then literally on stilts. Another method is to carry the columns on fairly large diameter cylinders sunk deeply into the ground.

New York pulsates with streams of traffic that threaten to turn the streets into chaos. Yet in this city, as in many others throughout the world, many great buildings and bridges have been erected with speed and efficiency and without hindrance to the never-ending flow of vehicles. In order to achieve this, the construction engineer must exercise his skill in logistics, which is the art and science of organizing every man, every machine, and every article to be in the right place at the right time. The variety of tasks demanded of the civil engineer is very great. At one time he may be required to thrust a railroad through uninhabited desert and pestilential jungle. At another, he may be required to build a great harbor or dam thousands of miles away. Yet again, he

Below, the Empire State Building towers above the skyscrapers of New York.

may be called upon to erect a great structure in the heart of a big city. Very different as the technical problems may be, the logistical problems are even more diverse.

In New York there stands the "Queen of Skyscrapers," the Empire State Building. Overwhelming in its sheer height, a long slender finger pointing to the heavens, eminent and majestic on the famous New York skyline, it is by far the tallest building in the world. Containing 102 storeys, the building itself is 1250 feet high. Surmounting it, there is a television tower 222 feet tall, making the total height 1472 feet. The structural steel framing contains 58,000 tons. It took a further 13 million bricks, 2 million square feet of limestone facing☞, 70,000 cubic yards of concrete, and great quantities of other materials to build it. The total load on the foundations is 300,000 tons, and the load on the huge columns was so tremendous that they were observed to have shortened $6\frac{1}{4}$ inches at the 85th floor. The building had to be constructed with great speed in one of the busiest spots in the world, and the supply and erection of these prodigious quantities of materials, all converging on this one central spot, were planned with great precision.

An intricate program was worked out, coordinating the rate of supply with the scheduled speed of construction. The phasing had to be perfect; if it was not, then either construction would lag behind or the New York streets would become chaotic. It worked, and the people of New York saw the vast structure growing day by day, scarcely aware how those great masses of material got there.

A study of some of New York's skyscrapers would convince you that in modern buildings the walls no longer act as supports. To overcome the strong vibrations from subway trains passing near the foundations, the steel frames are taken down below the level of the tunnels and anchored in the solid rock underlying Manhattan. The walls are hung on the frame, but they do not touch the ground where the vibrations occur. The Waldorf Astoria Hotel is a good example. Walking around it, you see a gap between the bottom of the walls and the pavement.

The Pirelli skyscraper in Milan is of most modern concrete design. A tall resplendent shaft, 32 storeys high, it is more or less cigar-shaped in plan. It is constructed in reinforced and prestressed concrete☞. Four massive elongated columns extending across the structure carry the building and solve the difficult wind resistance problems. Special account was taken of the severe torsional strains to which such a delicately proportioned building is subject. In order to check the calculations, a $\frac{1}{15}$th scale model was first tested in the laboratory. And now the finished structure stands, giving expression to the words of a famous French architect who spoke of "the accumulation of very beautiful things in which economic law reigns supreme, and mathematical exactness is joined to daring and imagination. That is beauty."

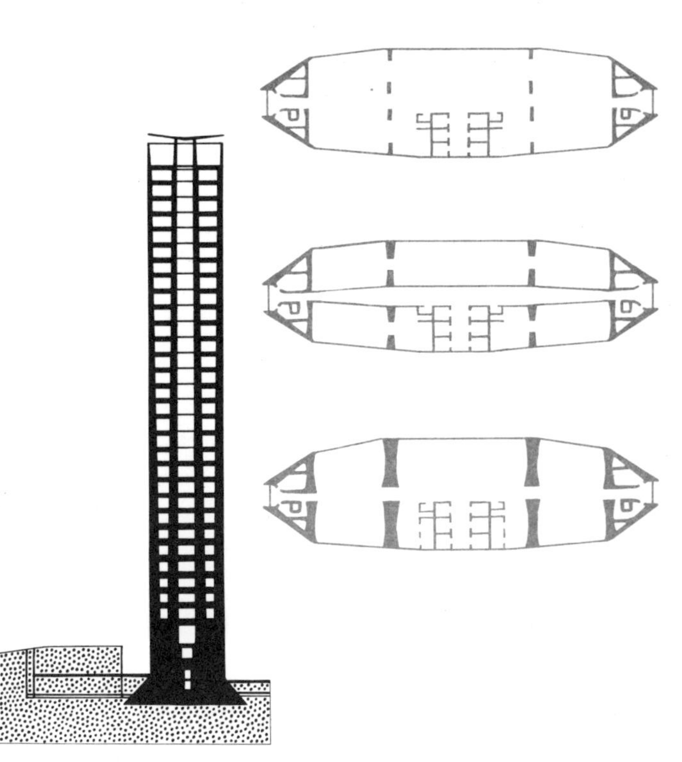

The Pirelli skyscraper, Milan. Its 32 floors are cantilevered from four tall columns (center), which taper toward the top, as the sections show.

Inside the underground Basilica of St. Pius X, Lourdes. Diagrams show the church in ground plan (upper) and in cross section through line ab (lower).

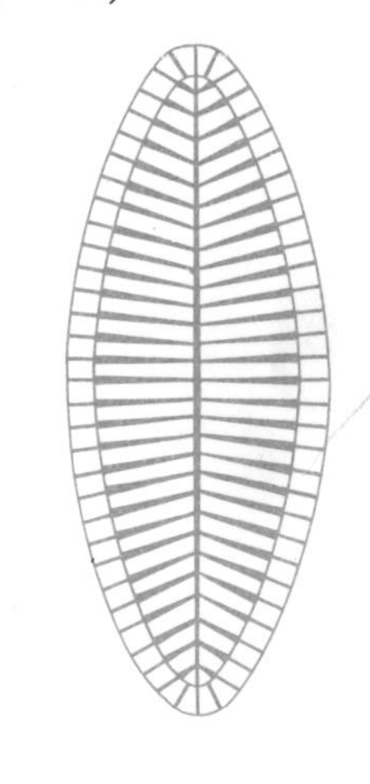

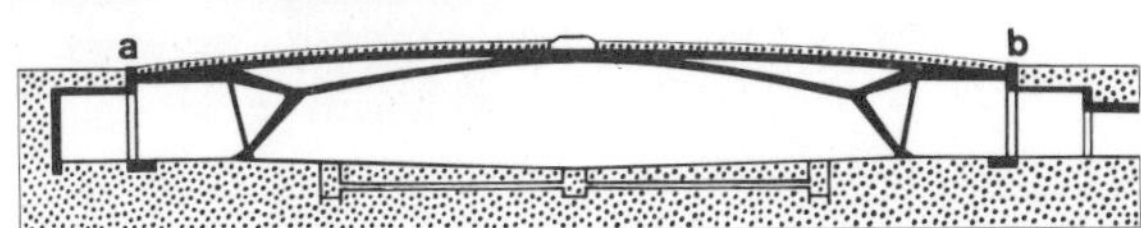

Millions of pilgrims have visited Lourdes in the French Pyrenees. Since the early part of 1958, the centenary of the apparitions, they have worshiped in the new Basilica of St. Pius X. Sunk into the ground and turfed over, the church lies under a green meadow, preserving the harmony of the Grotto of Massabeile and the sanctuaries nearby. Twenty thousand worshipers gather around the central altar and offer their devotions in this striking and original example of modern prestressed concrete construction. Looking around, they perceive the symbolically oval shape of the building which reminds them of the fish symbol of the early Christians, and of the halo of Christ in Majesty as represented in the Byzantine and Roman churches. The tracery of slender beams and arches above their heads, the network of struts☞ and braces☞ in the aisles around them, modern in feeling though they are, have beauty and reverence.

The big radio telescope at Jodrell Bank in England is one of the largest of its kind working today. Its great rotating bowl is 250 feet in diameter, and it can probe millions of light-years into space. The structure is in steel and it weighs 2000 tons. It is designed to withstand gales of 100 miles an hour, as well as vibrational effects or structural flutter☞. Two 20-ton derrick cranes☞, mounted on steel towers to give a 250-foot lift, were used to erect this telescope.

Probably the tallest structure in the world today is the steel television tower for station KTHI-TV in North Dakota in the United States of America, which is 2063 feet high. Built in 1963 at a cost of half a million dollars, it took only 30 days to erect.

Building the roof of Rome's Palazzo dello Sport from precast concrete units.

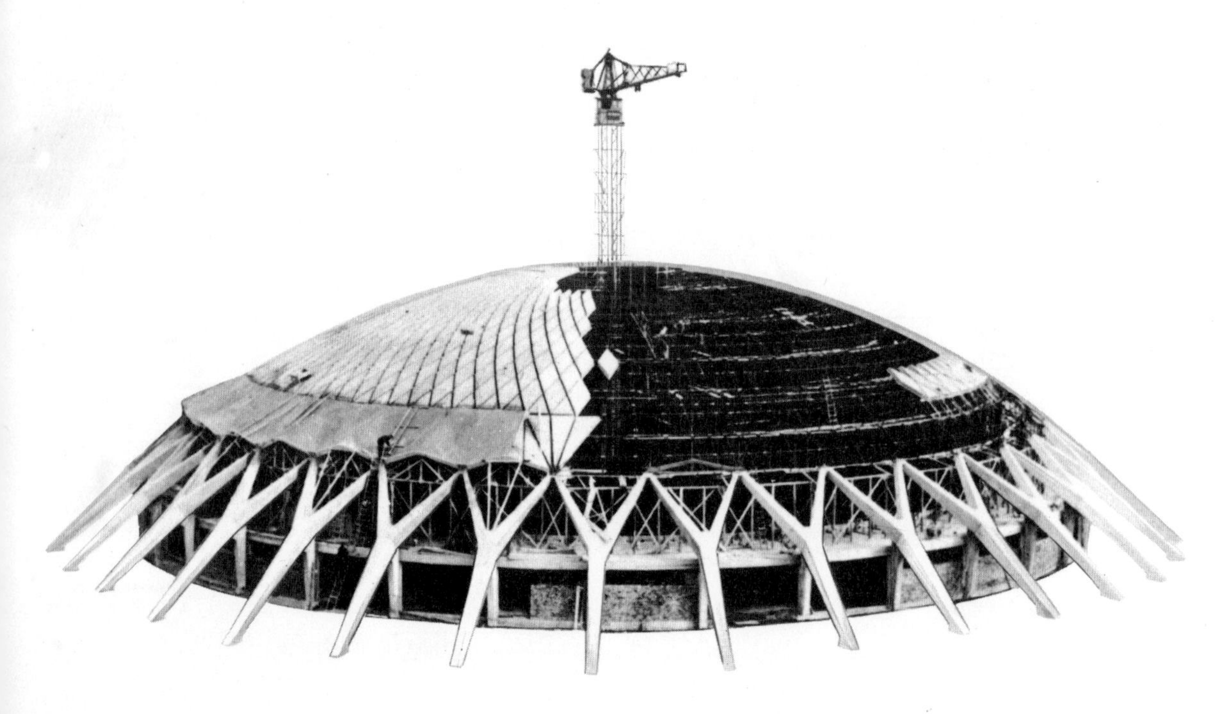

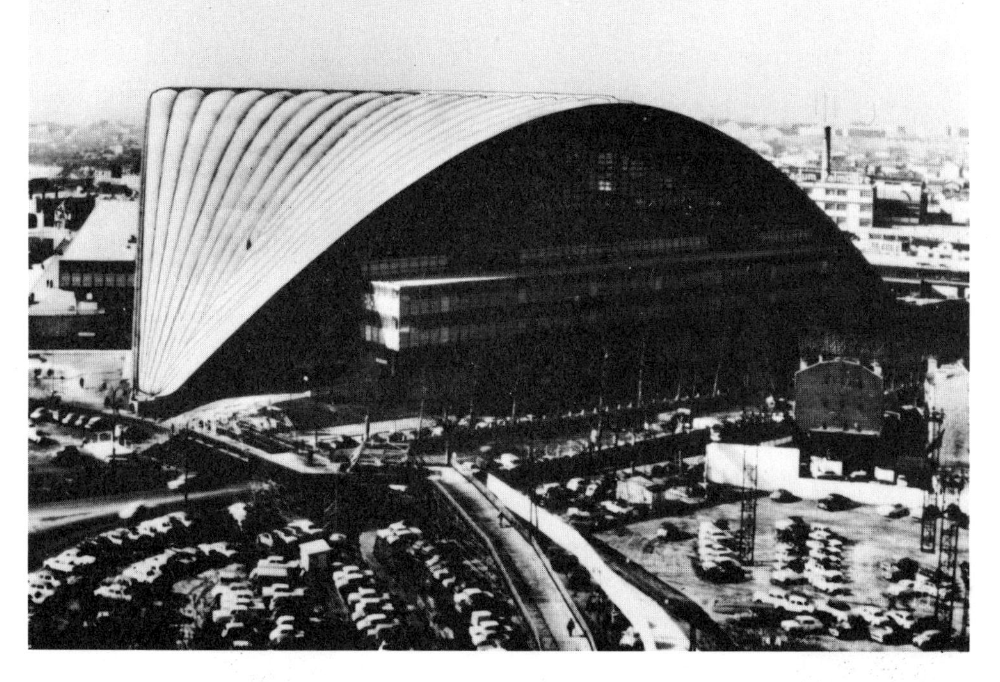

The triangular-based concrete roof of the C.N.I.T. exhibition hall, Paris.

In contrast with these steel structures, we find concrete being put to new uses in modern building. Since concrete when it is poured takes on a plastic form before it sets hard, it can be used to build up all kinds of complicated shapes. Concrete beams and columns are now often used instead of steel in the framework of large buildings. One reason for this is that concrete is cheaper as a material. Besides, it does not require as much skill in handling; to erect a steel framework, we must have expensive riveting gear and the men to work it.

In Rome, the Palazzo dello Sport built for the 1960 Olympics is a grand example of the Italian genius for building in concrete. It has an imposing and beautiful dome that is supported around its lower edge by a system of raking struts and braces.

The great hyperbolic concrete cooling towers that are a feature of English power stations are also supported on raking columns. One wonders how those great shells, 300 feet and more in height, can be supported by such frail-looking members. In this case, the main purpose of the open strut system is to permit a current of air to enter and rise up the interior of the cooling towers.

The spectacular modern exhibition hall on the outskirts of Paris is the biggest building in that city, and covers some five and a half acres. The vast spreading roof rises in the angle of two avenues. It is a triangular-based double concrete shell springing from the ground at three points only, and the design is similar to that of an airplane wing.

4 Roads and Airfields

From Asia Minor to Spain, from Central Europe to North Africa, the great achievement of the Romans was to build some 50,000 miles of roads for the consolidation of their Empire and the governing of its peoples. From Canada to Mexico, from the Atlantic to the Pacific, the people of the United States have built over 3,600,000 miles of roads for the opening up of their country and for its full development as an industrial nation.

It all began with routes such as the Wilderness Road to Kentucky, the Natchez Trace to Nashville, the Santa Fe Trail, the Oregon Trail, and the Overland Trail, names that thrill us still. Today the names are gone; and the roads of America carry numbers. But new names and a new kind of thrill have arisen; the names and the thrill of machines. The making of roads today is almost completely mechanized and it is to American engineers that we owe many of our modern road machines and methods. We have entered an era in which the labor of men has given way to powerful machines designed to carry out all kinds of specialized tasks with speed and accuracy.

An English poet once sang of the time when "the rolling English drunkard made the rolling English road." In those days, roads swung around hills and obstacles and switchbacked up hill and down dale. They had a charm of their own, but they have become unsuited to the fast and heavy road traffic that has arisen since.

The fast highways of the world today have relatively flat gradients; they dispense entirely with bends, and such curves as they have are very gradual. Many penetrate hills and mountains, cross valleys and ravines; and a great deal of excavation and fill☞ are necessary if they are to be kept reasonably straight and not too steep. Fortunately, modern methods of mechanical excavation both in "dirt" (or "muck") and in rock are fast and economical, so that nowadays the location engineer can plan with confidence routes involving large quantities of excavation.

Four-level freeway interchange at Los Angeles, California.

Though many mountain roads are planned to climb steeply and wind sharply to avoid the enormous amount of excavation that would otherwise be required, a surface route sometimes becomes virtually impossible. Then the only thing to do is to tunnel through the mountains, or span the cliffs.

Let us look at a large mountain road excavation project, the Rogers Pass route through the Canadian Rockies. More than 90 miles long, it shortens by 100 miles the old Trans-Canada Highway Big Bend route along the Columbia River. At one time, this area was considered impractical as a highway route, but modern machinery and modern methods have changed this. The entire length involved 15 million cubic yards of soft excavation and 7 million cubic yards of rock excavation.

While the Rogers Pass route as a whole set many problems characteristic of mountain work, the major problems lay in the 27-mile section through the Glacier National Park. Here, in a narrow valley surrounded by towering mountains, is the heart of the avalanche country. In rain, silty material becomes a soft unworkable mud, bogging everything down. Muskeg swamps near the summit of the pass gave the engineers many a headache. The country is under ice and snow in the winter, so that work could go on only in the short summer. In the spring, when the thaw set in, the melting ice brought down dangerous avalanches. Heavy runoff of melting snow and water from the mountain tops poured down the steep slopes of the sidehill cuts and turned them into a quagmire that hindered both men and machines.

The route cuts into the steep mountain sides far above the valley below. Men clearing the ground ahead, and drilling the rock for blasting, had to work with ropes around their waists; the ropes were tied to anchors above. Bulldozers☞ cut a narrow "bench" or shelf in the mountainside to serve as a footing for the main excavation machines, which followed and widened it out to the full width. These bulldozers sometimes worked in pairs, one high above and well anchored down, holding the working bulldozer below by a strong wire rope. The men call this arrangement the "Yo-Yo." They never seem to mind the dangerous nature of their work; they never seem to consider that the steel rope might break. Perhaps they know their engineers have worked it all out carefully and watch everything like hawks.

Excavation is the job of moving soil and rock. There are many different kinds of soil to be shifted, and vastly differing conditions of site and climate in which this work must be carried out. There are obvious differences between scraping sand in an arid desert and draglining mud and silt☞ in a marsh; between blasting hard granite from the side of an icebound mountain and ripping the softer shales and sandstones in a summer valley; between struggling with wet sticky clay and moving waterlogged gravel. But knowledge of the machines and techniques

Road-making machines: (1) tractor with scraper for tearing up and hauling away soil; (2) dumper; (3) compactor; (4) excavating tractor; (5) grader.

required to deal with such variety is not enough. The civil engineer must also turn to geology and to the new science of soil mechanics. There is no one way of handling excavation problems: each project must be dealt with on its merits.

Let us now turn to a typical example of this kind of work, on a section of US 40, northeast of San Francisco. It is early in the morning. The sun is low over the horizon and the job is beginning to hum. Diesel engines start up, whine, splutter, and then burst into a roar. Tough foremen bark orders, sleepy-eyed young engineers adjust their levels☞ or theodolites☞, and the big "cats" go to work.

They took little more than 500 day and night shifts. In that time they excavated nearly 10 million cubic yards of tough shale and sandstone out of one huge cutting☞ a quarter of a mile wide through a hill 250 feet high, and also 1½ million cubic yards from two smaller "bumps" further on. They had first to tear up the shale and sandstone with wicked-looking hydraulic rippers mounted on some of the big "cats." Then they put the rubber-tired tractors and scrapers☞ to work, some of them in tandem, digging up the ripped material. Crawler tractors pushed them while they were loading, for the earth was obstinate, causing the tires of the big vehicles to spin. Then away they roared, their tires singing, at speeds of 30 miles an hour and more, over haul roads tended and nursed by graders☞ to make their paths swift and easy. Arriving at the fill, they dumped their loads in layers, turned, and sped back again for more—on the move all the time.

Day and night they worked, stopping only for refueling, for a tire check, for some mechanical adjustment, or for handing over to the next shift. At the fill, bulldozers spread the dumped loads thinly and sheepsfoot rollers☞ hauled by crawler tractors did the initial compaction☞, or packing down, in a number of passes. Next, a grader turned the material over and spread it out. To prepare for compaction, a tanker sprinkled water on it. Finally a huge rubber-tired compactor followed, circling in pass after pass until the material was packed hard, reaching the specified 90 percent density. Only then could the engineers be sure that the fill would settle no further, and that the road to be laid on top would be safe.

All this time the scrapers were speeding to and from the big cut, depositing more and more material in the fills, while the great scar in the hillside grew deeper and wider. How the Roman road-makers would have stared in wonder at all this strange activity!

Once the engineers have cut through the hills and filled in the valleys to provide the subgrade☞, they are ready to begin work on the subbase☞ and road pavement. There are several ways of building these. But since today's road traffic is becoming heavier in weight and volume, road pavements must be made stronger and more uniform. Therefore concrete☞ is generally used for the highways of today. Construction

Laying a concrete road pavement: first, paver dumps concrete on subgrade . . .

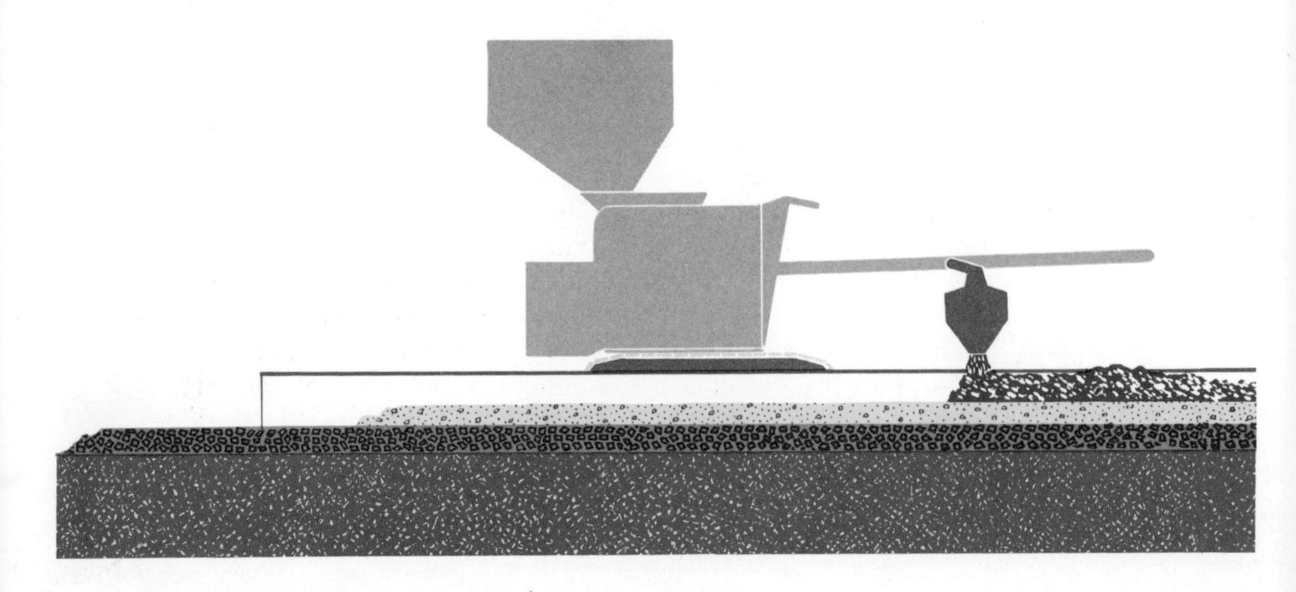

work is almost completely mechanized. With concrete this is essential, for concrete is an artificial material that is best made and put in place by machines.

We can imagine a typical concrete paving job. It could be one of the great American expressways, or the M1 in England. It could be a German *autobahn* or an Italian *autostrada*. On any of these jobs you would see the manufacture of the concrete begin at the quarry where the rock is blasted out and broken up into small pieces by a series of crushers. These pieces of rock are passed over screens that sort them out into different sizes. From the crushing and screening plant, the stone is taken to the batcher, a tall tower-like structure where the correct proportions of each size of stone, together with sand and cement, are automatically weighed out.

Next, you would see the batched ingredients of the concrete taken to the paver☞, a large twin drum concrete mixer traveling on caterpillar tracks. The paver receives these ingredients in one of the mixing drums, churns them around to mix them thoroughly, adds the precise amount of water (no more or the concrete would be too weak, no less or it would be too stiff and unworkable), then deposits the mixed concrete into a bucket in front of it. When full, the bucket travels out on a long steel boom attached to the paver and then drops its contents onto the subgrade of the lane being paved.

Next, the concreting train comes into operation. First, the spreader☞ moves into position and spreads the concrete uniformly over the width of the lane. Its screed strikes off the concrete closely to its finished level. Then the finisher follows, screeding the concrete again and even more closely. Finally, you would see the "float finisher" which floats, or smooths, the concrete to its final accuracy.

. . . *then a spreader distributes the concrete evenly. Next comes a finisher, to* screed *or shape the surface, then a float finisher to give the final touch.*

There are, of course, variations between these jobs, depending where the highway is being constructed—for example, in the design of the subbase, thickness of paving, machinery, and the like. Before the highway reached completion, you would have seen workmen carrying out several subsidiary processes; for instance, making joints for expansion and contraction of the concrete under extremes of temperature, preventing it drying out too quickly, and so on. But in all cases you would have been impressed by the almost complete mechanization of the entire job, with only one or two men following behind, giving a finishing touch to some minor blemish left by the machines. One is reminded of the advice given by one experienced construction engineer: "Think in terms of machines not of men, and if you can't find a machine to do the job, sit down and invent one."

Roads and airfields are used for very different purposes, but to the civil engineer there are no important technical differences. The general excavation and paving procedures are similar, and the differences are largely in the dimensions.

The pavement of a four-lane concrete road is usually about 50 feet wide and rarely more than 10 inches thick. A heavy bomber runway may be two or three times as thick, and up to 12,000 feet long and 300 feet wide. The main difference is that an airfield must be made level over an area considerably wider than its runways; and to provide modern aircraft with safe approaches, excavation may be considerable at the ends of the runways. So far as possible, then, airfield sites are chosen on level ground. But what do you do when there are mountains close by and all available land is occupied?

The planning of the Kai Tak Airport in Hong Kong was complicated and largely determined by the mountainous topography of the area. The Hong Kong district is very crowded and there is very little flat land. The engineers therefore adopted the ingenious idea of building the main runway in the sea!

One approach is from the southeast and is a straight-instrument run from the sea through the Lei Mun Gap between Hong Kong Island and the mainland. To avoid the inland mountains, the other approach is over the sea and along the coast from the west, and involves a 40-degree turn followed by a 3000-foot straight run to the touchdown threshold. This unique approach was thoroughly tested before it was finally adopted. The runway is built as a promontory 8500 feet long and 800 feet wide, jutting out into the bay. To make this artificial promontory, some 10 million cubic yards of sand were dredged from the sea bottom and pumped between massive protective walls of rock rising 50 feet from the seabed. A further 3 million cubic yards of decomposed granite were dug out of the hills on the mainland and dumped on the upper portion of the promontory.

Hauling such a large quantity of granite by a fleet of dump trucks through the narrow streets of Kowloon presented a severe problem. The only way to avoid delays, traffic jams, and accidents was to provide one road through the city for the big trucks; it was fenced off completely from other traffic. Also, special bridges were built for cross traffic and pedestrians.

Instead of using concrete, the engineers decided on a flexible pavement for the runway, since it would better withstand settlement of the dredged fill. This flexible pavement was given a 14-inch-thick base course of densely graded crushed stone thoroughly rolled and packed firm. On top of this they laid an asphalt☞ surface $4\frac{1}{2}$ inches thick. A special feature of this airport is the intricate system of approach and runway lighting to guide the planes in at night, especially along the turn in from the west.

London Airport: 30,000 feet of runways with a concrete pavement 2 feet deep.

5 Bridging the Waters

The modern bridge is a mark of our civilization. Today, we build double-deck bridges, bridges that lift, and bridges that swing. We take old bridges down and put new ones in their place without interrupting traffic. We raise or lower them bodily and we move them sideways. We pick up and set heavy bridge sections with winches☞ and mammoth cranes☞. We float bridges into position, and we roll them in. We jack and we pull and we push bridges weighing thousands of tons. We build beautiful bridges and ugly bridges. We can build a concrete arch of 1000-foot span, and a steel suspension bridge☞ spanning 4260 feet.

Tomorrow, our theory tells us, with our present materials we will be able to build a concrete arch spanning one mile, and a steel suspension bridge spanning two miles. With new materials and subtler theories, our scope will reach almost beyond imagining. But though man's strategy in his struggle with nature is growing bolder, it is never reckless; everything is carefully pondered and calculated beforehand.

The first thing the engineer must consider is the foundation☞: on this depends the stability of his bridge. Severe problems can arise with bridge foundations, for rivers naturally tend to carve their way through the weaker and softer strata making up the river bed. The waters often deposit thick layers of silt☞. The engineer must then dig through the silt in order to strike firm ground beneath.

There are three basic types of bridges: beam or girder bridges; arch bridges☞; and suspension bridges. In a *simply supported* beam, the two ends rest on their supports. A *continuous beam* is joined at one or more intermediate supports. A *cantilever☞ beam* has no support at one end, and therefore must be anchored down at the other. A *truss* is a type of beam built from a number of pieces or members☞ to form a series of connected triangles, giving strength combined with lightness.

Beam bridges exert a simple downward pressure on their supports. Because of its shape, an arch bridge thrusts or pushes hard against its

Finishing one of the main cables of the Verrazano-Narrows Bridge, New York.

ends; its stability therefore requires ground firm enough to take these inclined thrusts. A suspension bridge is basically a rope from which the bridge deck☞ is hung. The rope passes over two towers and then to anchors on each side of the river. Their inclined pull is in contrast with the inclined push of an arch against its abutments☞.

The great bridges of today have grown from these basic types of structures. They stand as tributes to the vision of the men who first conceived such projects, to the imagination of the designers who prepared the plans and to the art of the builders.

But no engineer would be so rash as to think his bridge will never be bettered. He knows it is but a matter of time for new materials and techniques to come to the fore, and then his earlier efforts will be outdone. When the George Washington Bridge in New York was built, it had the world's longest span: 3500 feet across the Hudson River. It is still the heaviest suspension bridge, designed to take the biggest loads. Yet in the opening speech we find these words: "We are today inaugurating the building of the biggest bridge in the world. It won't be the biggest bridge very long, as time goes on." A year after this bridge was opened in 1931, engineers began work on a bridge 700 feet longer—the Golden Gate Bridge in San Francisco, California.

The entrance to San Francisco Bay is through a strait called the Golden Gate. It is aptly named, for it looks west across the ocean and in the light of a later summer evening the air is truly golden. Crossing this gap in a single graceful span of 4200 feet, the Golden Gate Bridge is one of the most exciting sights in the world. When the setting sun is reflected on the waters and the great bridge is outlined against the Pacific horizon, you understand what is meant by the "poetry of structure."

A few miles away, across the bay itself, soars the six-mile-long San Francisco-Oakland Bay Bridge. Its twin suspension bridges, each with 2310 feet central span and 1160 feet side spans, its great 1400-foot cantilever with its two 511-foot anchor spans, and its scores of smaller spans reaching for the Oakland shore, are all too vast and complex to be taken in with that single catch of the breath that the Golden Gate Bridge inspires. In its changing themes and intricacy of designs, here is a "symphony stretched across the waters." These two bridges are among man's greatest engineering achievements.

Four times in every 24 hours, the tidal currents sweep in and out beneath the Golden Gate at seven knots. Heavy seas and ocean storms batter against the two massive piers☞. The gigantic 746-foot-high towers, the two 36½-inch diameter cables, and the heavy 25-foot-deep stiffening trusses 220 feet above the waters, are subject to violent Pacific gales. These were the kinds of difficulties facing the engineers as they planned and built the south pier 1100 feet off-shore in 60 to 80 feet of water. Several times, storms swept away the work, or damaged it; several times, plans were changed as the engineers learned from their failures. In the end, the great pier, which was designed to carry a load of 325,000 tons on its foundations, emerged above the waters.

The huge steel towers of the Golden Gate Bridge were designed to resist a variety of forces—dead and live loads, temperature changes, wind, and earthquakes. Each tower contains 22,000 tons of steel and is made up of two large cellular box-shaped shafts☞ braced together at intervals. The towers were erected by two 85-ton capacity derricks☞ riding on a steel truss between the shafts. As sections of tower were added, the entire rig, cranes and truss included, was lifted bodily by winches to the next position. This was repeated some 20 times until the top was reached. The towers were then ready to receive the calculated load of nearly 30,000 tons on each shaft.

The main cables of a suspension bridge are so large that the only practical way to install them is to make them in position while the bridge is being built. The Golden Gate Bridge is suspended from two such cables, each weighing 10,000 tons and 7650 feet long. Each cable contains 27,572 wires made up in 61 strands, and there are 80,000 miles

Bridge types. Upper, simply supported beam (left) and continuous beam (right); center, balanced cantilever; lower, stone arch. Arrows represent thrust.

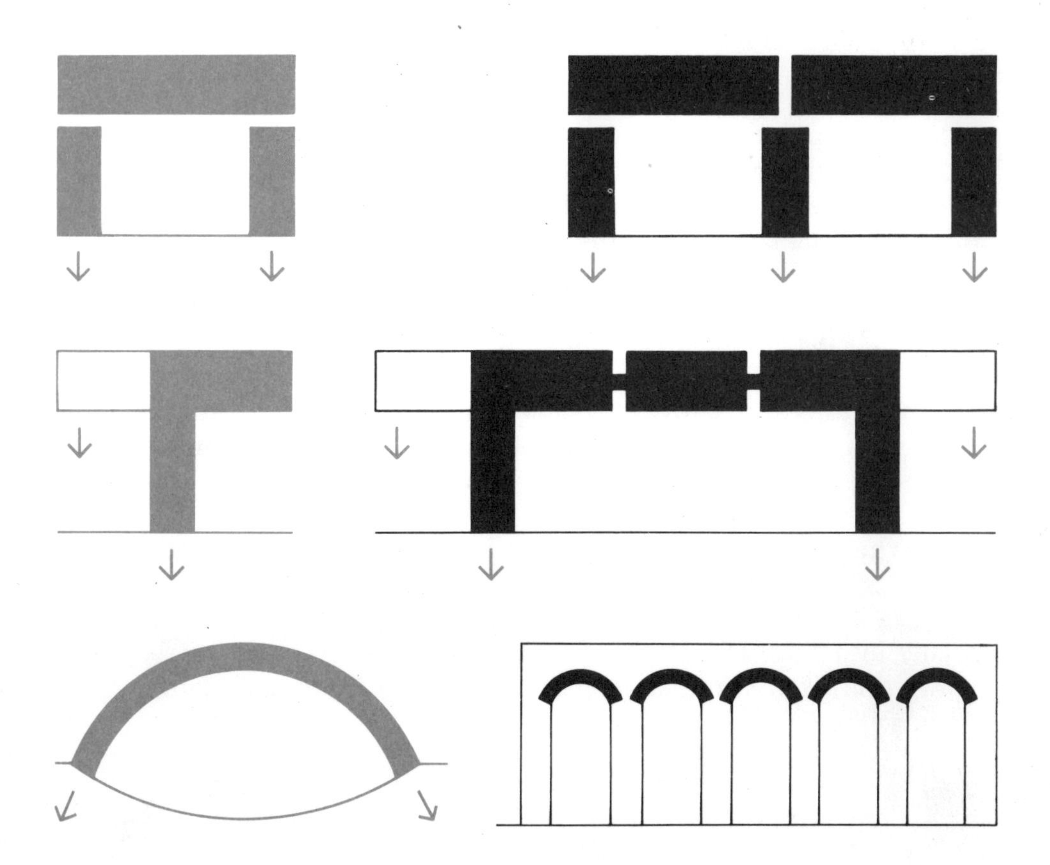

The Golden Gate Bridge, San Francisco, with 746-foot-high suspension towers.

of wire in the two cables. At the center, they sag 470 feet below the top of the towers, and each exerts a pull of 28,000 tons on its anchorages☞.

The first operation was to erect catwalks resting on a number of light steel ropes strung between the anchorages and over the tops of the towers. On these catwalks the men worked on the spinning of the main cables. Spinning consisted of hauling wires across the span by means of three spinning wheels mounted under a carriage attached to a haulage rope. The wire was fed from large reels stationed at the anchorages, the dead end being fastened to a shoe in the anchorage. A bight of wire was looped over each wheel which thus carried two wires across, the total amounting to six wires for each trip of the carriage. At mid-span, the wheels from each anchorage met and the wires were interchanged between the two anchorages. Each carriage was then pulled back again so that on its return each had completed the stringing begun by the other. When the spinning crew worked at top speed, they were placing 1000 miles of wire in a single shift. When spinning was completed, the cables were squeezed into circular shape by twelve hydraulic jacks☞ working in a ring. Finally came a wrapping of soft galvanized wire as a protection from wind, rain, and sea air. To finish the bridge, light

The San Francisco-Oakland Bay Bridge.

cranes erected stiffening trusses panel by panel, hanging them from the cables and moving out along the structure as fast as it grew.

On all counts, the San Francisco-Oakland Bay Bridge is a tremendous structure. A journey on one of its double decks is an experience to make one feel both proud and overawed. The giant girders of the cantilever tower high above the deck. The crisscross of wind bracing and the maze of structural members on all sides loom threateningly and then flash by. The cables of the suspensions rise and fall in a great steel cadence.

The twin suspension bridges across the West Bay provide a unique and imaginative solution to the problem of crossing a two-mile gap. Here, the engineers conceived two suspension bridges in "Indian file." The cables at the outer ends are anchored, as usual, on the shore on either side. But the problem was how to anchor the inner ends in the middle of the bay. The solution was magnificent in its boldness and simplicity: to build an artificial island of concrete in the middle of the bay and anchor the inner ends of the cables to it. That was the origin of "Central Anchorage W4," one of the most remarkable foundations yet attempted by man.

An ingenious variation of the standard caisson☞ technique was adopted. A huge caisson, or hollow bottomless box approximately 200 feet long by 100 feet wide, was constructed of steel, concrete, and timber. The largest ever used, it was floated out into position and held by steel hawsers attached to 26 heavy anchors. The depth of water was too great to follow the normal practice of first making the caisson high enough for the top to be above water when the cutting edge touched the bottom. So compressed air was pumped into 55 steel shafts which had been set in the caisson. This kept it buoyant. Gradually it was allowed to sink under the extra weight of the continuously extending concrete walls, whose tops were always kept above water. It grew taller and heavier and sank a foot or so every day, but it was kept floating and prevented from plunging to the bottom by increasing the air pressure.

Finally, weighing 31,000 tons, it landed on the mud bottom. It was then sunk to bedrock by dredging through the shafts. As it sank through mud and soft strata, the walls were continuously built up above water level. When it reached rock, engineers sealed the bottom with concrete deposited by special dump buckets, and the final anchorage pier was built up to above water level. Three of the main piers, also in the deepest part of the West Bay, were built in the same way.

The San Francisco-Oakland Bay Bridge: twin suspensions over the West Bay.

Long suspension bridges are too flexible for heavy rail traffic. For long spans, the steel cantilever and arch serve best. They are rigid enough to carry modern locomotives that may weigh up to 200 tons, and can stand up to the impact at rail joints, the swaying of engines, and the lateral pressure or "nosing" of flanged wheels on the rails and on the bridge.

Two of the biggest cantilevers ever built are the Quebec Bridge with its 1800-foot main span, completed in 1918, and the Howrah Bridge in Calcutta with a 1500-foot main span, completed in 1943. In these bridges the cantilever portions are balanced by anchor spans tied down to foundations.

At Quebec, a crane of over 900 tons moved out from each end toward the center. Each traveled on the big cantilever trusses it erected in front of itself. Each cantilever arm ended 580 feet from the supporting towers. Between the ends there was a 640-foot gap, to be filled by a suspended span weighing 5000 tons. This span was built in a yard nearby and floated under its final position on barges. Winches then hauled it up with wire rope "falls" attached to its ends.

The Verrazano-Narrows Bridge, New York, with a single span of 4260 feet.

On the Howrah Bridge, the cranes, weighing a little over 600 tons, crept out on the top booms of the cantilevers. The arms each projected 468 feet over the river, while the suspended span between them was 564 feet long and weighed 4000 tons. Here, the center span was in two halves, each built as an extension of the two cantilevers. This left an 18-inch gap at the center. Hydraulic jacks then pushed the two halves together. Never before had this been tried on so large a bridge.

The great steel arch over Sydney Harbor, Australia, was also built by a crane on each side creeping out on the top boom, erecting sections of the arch forward of itself. Since arch sections are not stable until

The 1650-foot steel arch of Sydney Harbor Bridge, Australia.

they meet in the center, each side was temporarily anchored back into a tunnel by 128 large steel ropes. This enormous arch has a 1650-foot span, two feet short of the record held by the Bayonne Arch in America. It is, however, much heavier and higher, and carries a far heavier loading. Further, the Bayonne Arch spans shallow water, and therefore could be supported on trestles during construction. Before the two halves of the Sydney Harbor arch met in the center, they were projecting 800 feet over the river and 450 feet above the water. At this stage, each half weighed 14,000 tons and each had a 600-ton crane perched on its end. The situation was delicate and tense, for until the two halves were connected, only the anchorage cables held them up.

We may imagine the feelings of the engineers who had planned the operations. Would their calculations for the strength of the anchorage cables prove correct? Was the sandstone rock in the anchorage tunnels really as strong as they had reckoned? Was there anything wrong with their computations and measurements to ensure that the two halves of the arch would meet? Above all, would a storm arise just before the closure and while the two 800-foot half-arches were still free? In a similar situation, during the building of the highly original Tubular Bridge across the Menai Straits in Wales, Stephenson recorded: "at night I would lie tossing about seeking sleep in vain. The tubes filled my head. I went to bed and got up with them."

The Tubular Bridge over the Menai Strait, North Wales (built 1845-50).

The Sydney Harbor Arch engineers must have felt much the same. Years of work and millions of pounds hung on this moment. And then a violent gale arose and blew full on one side of the two half-arches. As the wind howled round the great masses of steel, the ends of the unfinished arch swayed slowly and frighteningly sideways, a few inches past each other. But the bridge held, and when the gale died down, the engineers, sleepless but happy, made the final moves for closure. The two halves of the arch had been erected somewhat higher than their final position, and the anchorage cables were slacked out to lower the ends so that they would meet.

It became a race against temperature, for as the sun went down, the great masses of steelwork cooled and contracted and the ends moved further apart. Extreme care was necessary: the cables could not be slacked out too quickly, or the 14,000-ton masses of steel might get a "run" and then nothing could stop them. In the end the engineers closed the bridge and found they had achieved amazing precision.

All these bridges have spans so large that no other material but steel would do. But for small and medium spans, steel is being ousted by prestressed concrete☞. The stresses☞ in a bridge arise from dead and live loads, wind forces, temperature changes, and so on. They produce either compression or tension; steel stands up well to both. Ordinary concrete, on the other hand, can resist only moderate compressive forces, and it is weak in tension. To overcome this, steel rods are buried in the concrete, which is then called reinforced concrete☞. A reinforced concrete beam shares its work between the two materials, the concrete taking the compression and the steel rods the tension.

In prestressed concrete, the concrete is artificially put into compression before any load from the structure comes upon it. The concrete can then resist tension up to the extent of the compression that was put into it beforehand: an applied tension partly undoes the precompression. The principle is similar to the trick of picking up several bricks or blocks of wood at a time by pressing them hard together. The compressive prestress is put into concrete by high tensile steel rods or wire. These are drawn taut by hydraulic jacks and then fastened to the ends of the concrete member. The tension on the wire pulls the two ends of the concrete together, thus compressing it.

Since concrete in its initial stages is a plastic material, concrete bridges have normally to be manufactured and built as a unit in their final position. This is called casting *in situ* and requires a temporary system of formwork☞, "centering," "stagings," and props to hold the concrete until it has set hard and become self-supporting. Prestressing is a new technique; its growth has brought forth a wealth of new ideas in bridge design and building methods. Precasting, for instance, can now be used in ways a few years ago no one thought possible.

The members of a precast structure are made beforehand and then lifted into place. While reinforced concrete members are usually very heavy, prestressed and precast members of the same strength are much lighter. Likewise for a given weight and strength, prestressed beams and slabs are longer. Besides, they stand up much better to handling and erection stresses.

The construction by French engineers of the 500-foot cast *in situ* concrete arch near Caracas in Venezuela was one of the boldest and most spectacular exploits in bridge engineering. It has been said of the way this bridge was built that "if the builder knew enough about the behavior of such a structure he would not dare to undertake it. Yet if he didn't know his business exceptionally well he couldn't complete it."

The crown of the arch is 220 feet above the gorge below. The normal way of building up falsework trestles from the bottom of the gorge

Cast in situ *concrete arch on the Caracas-La Guaiara highway, Venezuela.*

would have been extremely costly and slow. The quarter spans on each side were concreted out from the abutments on centering. Each side was supported by six temporary steel rope guys, anchored back to the massive vertical end piers also rising from the abutments. Between the quarter spans thus built remained a gap of half the span.

To complete this gap, the engineers hit on a daring solution never attempted before: they built the centering for the gap on the floor of the gorge 220 feet below the bridge. It was 265 feet long by 75 feet wide and weighed 250 tons. Four winches on the two ends of the completed quarter spans let down steel ropes or "falls" to be attached to the four corners of the 250-ton falsework structure below. After eight hours of cautious and steady lifting, the center arch falsework was eased into place and secured. In the concreting that followed, the engineers

The 24-mile-long Lake Pontchartrain Causeway near New Orleans.

worked with great care symmetrically from the center outward, to avoid any movements and sway. When the concrete had set, the falsework was lowered back to the floor of the gorge.

Over windswept Lake Pontchartrain, near New Orleans, there runs a bridge 24 miles long. A white concrete ribbon vanishing into the distance, it stands as a tribute to the imagination and skill of the bridge-builder. The bridge was completed in 1956; amazingly, it took only 15 months to build. This required mass production and assembly line ideas both in the design and in the construction.

Some figures will show the magnitude of the work: the total weight of the structure is approximately 600,000 tons. The bridge consists of 2215 identical bents☞, the constituent parts of which were precast on shore and barged out onto the lake where they were erected. Each bent is like a huge football goal and comprises two large cylindrical pre-stressed concrete piles☞ about 90 feet long and weighing over 30 tons. On top of the piles there rests a reinforced concrete cap (like the cross-bar of a goal) weighing 25 tons. Finally, spanning between caps is a prestressed concrete deck unit 56 feet long by 33 feet wide and weighing some 200 tons. The casting yard occupied 40 acres; it was a marvel of mechanization and streamlined production methods. Every detail was worked out beforehand, and the job was done at great speed.

As they came off the production lines, piles, caps, and deck units were loaded onto barges by large whirler and gantry☞ cranes, and towed out to the bridge. There, the 50-ton cranes mounted on pontoons each picked one pile up and set it in position on the lake bottom. A third pontoon equipped with powerful jetting pumps forced water at high pressure into the ground round the perimeter of the piles, thus loosening the ground and allowing them to sink some distance into the bed of the lake. After this, heavy piling hammers drove the piles hard until they could go no deeper. The 90-foot stilts penetrating far beneath the lake, were now ready to receive and carry the bridge. Next, another pontoon-mounted crane of 50-tons capacity fitted the caps on top of each pair of piles. Finally, there followed a 200-ton derrick barge, which set the massive deck units across the caps. Day after day, straight as an arrow, this bridge made for the far shore at unprecedented speed. At the peak, it grew half a mile a week.

The cantilevering out method, used widely in steel bridges, has the great merit of requiring no falsework. Bridge engineers have therefore tried to apply this method to concrete bridges, but they could not go ahead with it until prestressing came into wide use. The balanced cantilever system of construction for concrete bridges is simple and does not need the costly heavy cranes and special rigs of precast work. So far, only a few bridges have been built in this way, but the method is bound to come into wider use.

75
16543

6 Tunneling under the Mountains

Driving a tunnel is a venture into the unknown. The engineer can seldom be certain what awaits him except one thing—trouble. Ahead may lie soft and treacherous ground, fissures and faults, holes and cavities; icy subterranean rivers may freeze him, hot springs may scald him, high temperatures may roast him, rock falls and ground squeeze may crush him, or riverbeds above may collapse and drown him. These, and many more, are the dangers he must face.

The crews are set driving toward each other blindly, often from miles apart; yet they must "meet on a dime." In tunnel mythology, there is the tale of two crews who failed to meet and passed each other, and now must keep on forever in the vain hope of meeting one day. Maybe this was because one of the crews allowed a woman visitor: tunnel miners believe it unlucky to let women set foot in a heading☞.

The engineers begin by making a surface survey between two ends (called "portals" or "adits"), to determine the line of a drive. Usually, they dig intermediate shafts☞ along the line of the tunnel to open up more faces☞ and thus speed the work. At the portals it is easy to transfer the surface line into the heading and so keep the crews on line, since the engineer can sight his instruments directly from outside. But for headings starting from the bottom of a shaft, fixing the direction is much more difficult.

Two steel wires about $\frac{1}{50}$th of an inch in diameter, with heavy weights at the bottom, are suspended in the shaft. The distance between the wires, or "base," may be some 10 feet, but in small and crowded shafts it might well be less. On top, by means of his theodolite☞ or "transit," the engineer aligns the two wires with the surface line of the tunnel. Below, another engineer does the reverse, setting his transit dead in line with the two wires. He then projects this line into the heading. With a 10-foot base and a 2-mile drive, any error in lining up on the wires is multiplied over 1000 times.

Interior of the $7\frac{1}{4}$-mile-long Mont Blanc Tunnel between Italy and France.

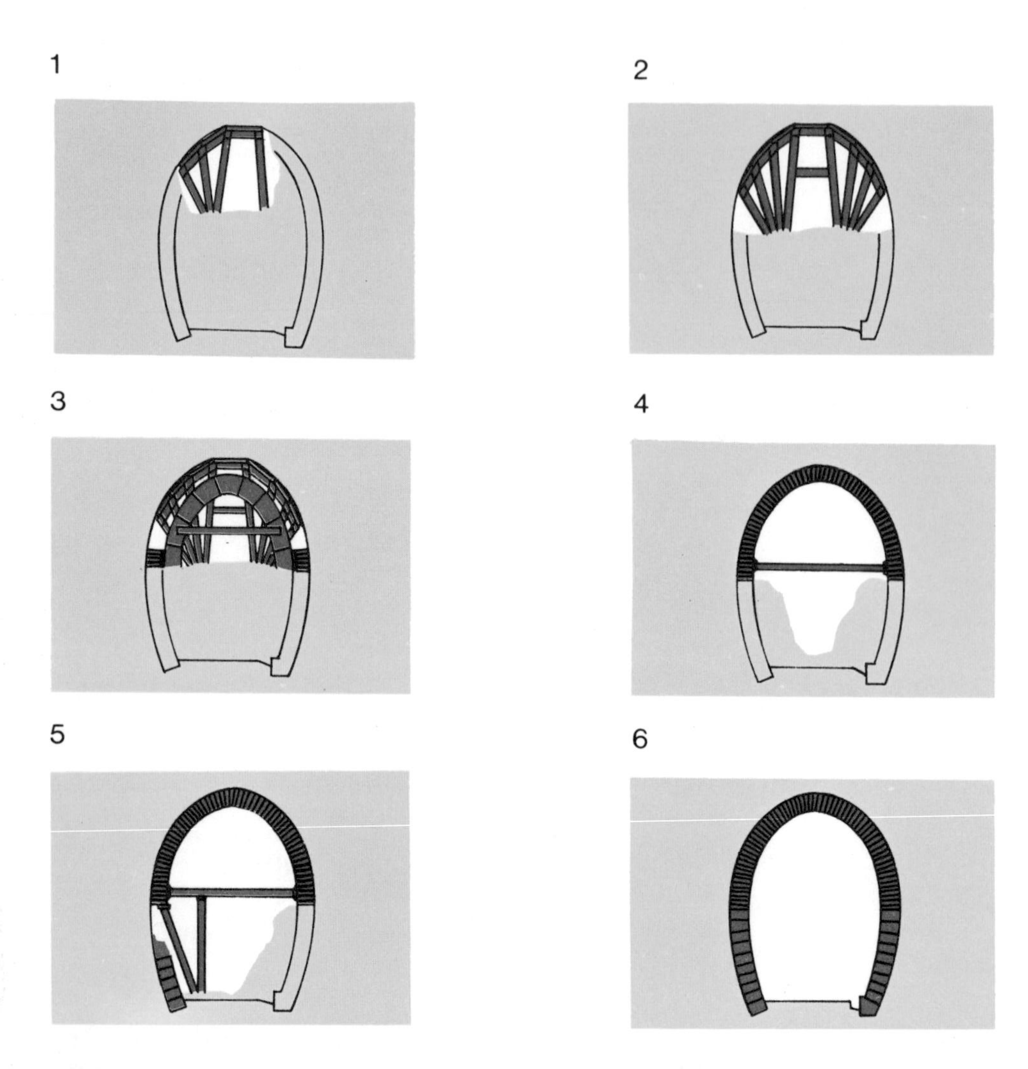

How the St. Gotthard Tunnel was built in 1872-81. Engineers began by driving a small top heading (1); then they widened it (2) and deepened it (3-6).

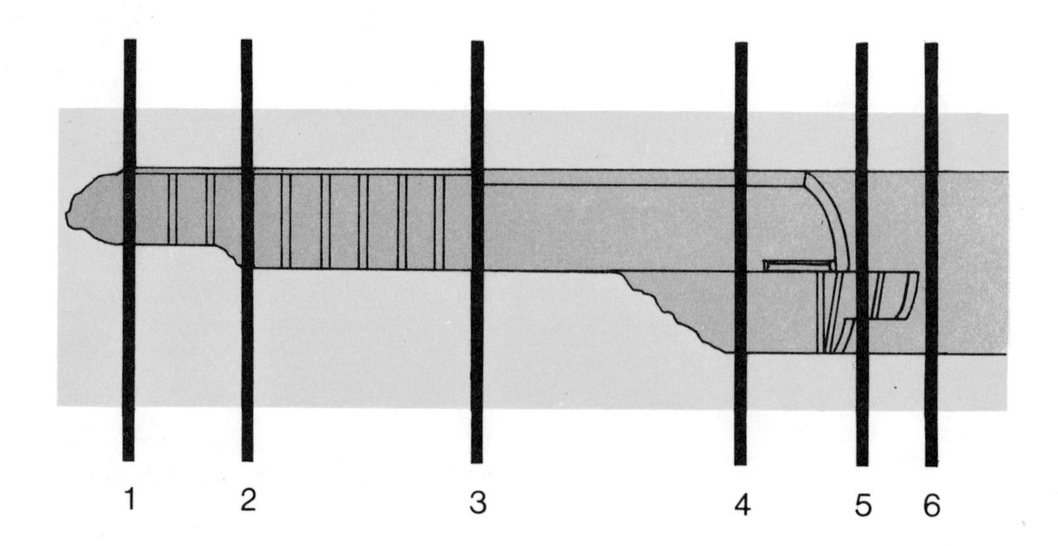

Drives of up to five or six miles from each end of a tunnel under mountains are not uncommon. The engineer must therefore work with accuracy and repeat the aligning many times. The job takes time, skill, and patience, and is usually hampered by tough conditions underground. But there is a feeling of triumph when the crews hole through, shake hands at the junction, and cheer when the check across shows they have met to a "gnat's whisker."

Few of the South Coast farmers who benefit from the water now flowing through the Tecolote Tunnel under the Santa Ynez mountains in California have heard of the battle fought on their behalf when it was built. The story of this tunnel is the story of a handful of unknown men whose guts and skill overcame one of the toughest drives in engineering history. Six and a half miles long and more than 2000 feet under the mountains, this tunnel, after a peaceful start, turned into a "vicious, snarling, fighting animal."

One day a sudden rush of water and sand broke through the face and quickly filled up hundreds of feet of the tunnel. An explosion of methane gas shook the tunnel from end to end and everyone ran for safety. All escaped, although some were slightly burned. They went back and built

Constructing a huge underground power station at Kemano, Canada.

Building a tunnel for the Loch Awe hydroelectric scheme (Scotland).

a heavy concrete☞ bulkhead to seal the tunnel. After pumping cement at high pressure into the ground ahead to consolidate it, they breached the bulkhead and dug on carefully, inch by inch, through the danger zone. But still the ground was running, still they met water and methane gas. More grouting was needed. After weary months, the crews finally struck better ground.

After a stretch of plain going, they decided to start on the opposite heading. Here, too, work began peacefully and then the crews struck an underground stream that poured 70,000 gallons an hour into the tunnel. Relying on the big tunnel pumps, the men worked their way slowly forward for more than half a mile, through water pouring in on all sides. Then they met faulted and broken shale and water at high pressure. The flow increased to 300,000 gallons an hour, driving the crews out. Again, they built heavy concrete bulkheads across the tunnel, and pumped cement into the ground ahead. Grouting pressures reached the unheard of figure of 2000 pounds a square inch; but this time the remedy failed. Water still cascaded in.

The engineers now decided to drive small tunnels, called drifts☞, on each side of the main tunnel to relieve the water pressure. Small drifts can be pushed slowly ahead where the main tunnel presents too large a surface under pressure. This plan worked, and slowly the main tunnel

Tunneling with a drum digger shield for a new subway line in London.

was driven ahead, keeping pace with the side drifts. After several hundred feet, they passed the broken ground, but much water was still pouring in. They tried to staunch the flow by pumping cement ahead. But then the water began to get hot and the temperature of the tunnel rose. Before long the water reached a temperature of 47°C, and the humidity at the face reached 100 percent. The flow instead of drying up, began to increase until 500,000 gallons an hour were pouring in, while gases escaping from the ground burned the men's eyes.

The engineers decided to stop work and draw up a new battle plan. They installed enormous pumps and boosters with special coolers for the compressed air machines, and the crews were set to work shorter shifts. To reach the face, now two and a half miles from the portal, the men rode up in rail mine cars filled with cool water, for protection against high temperatures. Through intense heat they drove the tunnel slowly forward, drilling, blasting, and "mucking," until they met the first heading.

Another famous water tunnel is the Lochaber Tunnel in Scotland. It is shaped like a horseshoe, 16 feet high and 21 feet wide, and merges into the rock side of Loch Treig more than 100 feet below the surface of the water. The tunnel carries water underground to a power station 15 miles away. The breakthrough into the lake presented an unusual problem: a final plug or barrier of rock between the tunnel and the lake had to be left and the whole blown out in one big blast. If the tunnel was driven too close to the lake, the water outside under great pressure might break through and drown all inside. If the plug was too thick, the attempt to blast it out in one shot might fail. Once the tunnel was filled with water, it would be impossible to get in again.

The miners, when within 85 feet of the lake, drilled forward pilot holes 35 feet long to test for fissures in the rock. These they grouted up with cement to prevent seepage. Then they drove ahead a small drift 5 feet high and 3 feet wide to explore the ground. The full section tunnel followed behind. Keeping pilot holes ahead of the face, they grouted up fissures as they met them. When the full tunnel section was 16 feet from the lake, the engineers, not daring to go any farther, prepared for the blast. A hundred and thirty-four holes were drilled into the barrier to within two feet of the water. In the floor in front of it they dug a deep, long sump☞ to receive the rock shot inward. Then they filled the holes with several tons of special high explosive and fired it. The blast blew out 3000 cubic yards of rock; shock waves 4 feet high churned the lake and the water rushed into the tunnel, speeding off on its 15-mile journey to the great turbines of the power station.

Subaqueous drives were long a tunneler's nightmare. The first to tackle one successfully was Brunel with his shield☞. This is an open steel cylinder pushed forward into the ground by hydraulic jacks☞. Inside it, the miners can work safely, digging out the ground ahead to ease the passage of the shield. The front end of a large shield is divided into compartments, each sealed with a door, so that the miners can dig away the face in small sections. As the shield is shoved forward, the permanent lining to the tunnel (cast iron or concrete rings) is erected behind.

When Brunel dug his famous River Thames Tunnel more than 100 years ago, compressed air for tunnels was unknown; it is thus not surprising that the river broke in quite a number of times. Today, compressed air is widely used by the civil engineer. Combined with the shield, it has enabled him to tunnel in water-bearing ground under rivers.

When compressed air is pumped into a tunnel, it counterbalances the pressure of the water that may be trying to pour in. The greater the height of water above the heading, the higher the air pressure must be. Exact balance is essential: if the air pressure is too low, the river will force its way into the tunnel. If the air pressure is too high, or a pocket in the ground is met, or the "cover" to the riverbed decreases suddenly, the air will force its way out through the face and the riverbed, making a hole in them and causing what tunnel miners fear above all else—a "blow." This may happen with such swift violence that men at the face may be shot out through the hole into the river.

With the sudden rush of compressed air, the pressure falls, and the water, no longer held back, pours into the tunnel. In the river, a boiling

The Italian entrance to the Mont Blanc road tunnel.

caldron of air and water tells its tale. Now the miners begin the fight of their lives! They call on the compressor men to pump more and more air into the tunnel. Held back by their mates from being swept away, they stuff sacks, hay, mud, shirts, coats, and anything to hand into the hole to fill it and so stop the blow. Sometimes they win; but very often they fail and must retreat, half drowned and covered in mud, to the safety of the emergency air lock, leaving the tunnel to fill up. The engineer then tries to seal the blow by dumping barge loads of clay on the riverbed; it may take thousands of tons to lay such a blanket. Air pressure is then turned on again, the miners go back, clean up the tunnel, and drive on.

But working in compressed air has other dangers: a man's blood and tissues become saturated with nitrogen, which forms bubbles when he leaves the tunnel. In compressed air he feels no ill effects, but if he decompresses too quickly, the bubbles cannot disperse and he may suffer severe pains known as "the bends." To avoid this, he must leave through an air lock, a chamber sealed off from both the tunnel and the outside. Here he waits while the pressure is lowered to that of the atmosphere.

7 Shelter for Ships

The long arms of the breakwaters☞ protect the harbor from the open sea. Outside, the storm hurls its fury on everything that stands in its way. Whipped by the gale, waves of 30 feet or higher explode against the rock and concrete☞ walls of the breakwaters, throwing spray 100 feet into the air. Within the harbor, their voyages over, ships ride their moorings in peace.

Storm and tempest, wind and waves, are among the great destructive forces of nature: concrete blocks weighing hundreds of tons can be tossed about like driftwood, and sections of a breakwater weighing thousands of tons can be bodily shifted.

Before he begins to build a breakwater, the civil engineer must study the action of waves, winds, tides, and currents around the harbor. None of these is yet completely understood. But hydraulics☞, meteorology, and hydrography☞ help the harbor engineer to build with growing confidence. In recent years, he has begun to build and test scale models to study his projects in the laboratory under artificial winds, waves, tides, and currents; and to observe the effects on nearby coastlines: silting, erosion☞, and littoral drift☞.

A good example of a discovery made from the study of laboratory models is the tetrapod☞. Invented by French engineers, it is made of concrete, and consists of four legs extending from a central hub. Normally, the exposed face of a breakwater is protected, or "armored," by large lumps of irregularly shaped quarried rock or by large concrete blocks. The regular cubic shape of concrete block, though often used, is too smooth; and large irregular pieces are hard to quarry. In any case, the pieces tend to slide on one another under the force of the waves, and to shift with under-pressure when the wave recedes. When tetrapods are dumped at random to form a layer, their shape gives hydraulic roughness to the surface of the breakwater, thus helping to dissipate the energy of the waves. Although the sea may shift the surface, the layer remains

The modern breakwater and docks of Marseilles Harbor, southeast France.

porous, and under-pressure dissipates; and as the legs of the tetrapods are designed to interlock, even a powerful wave cannot easily break it.

Rota harbor in the Bay of Cadiz in Spain, completed in 1959, has one of the most modern breakwaters. For the inner section, 2000 feet long, where the water is shallow and waves are lower than 10 feet, the protective layer consists of pieces of rock or riprap☞, weighing from 3 to 8 tons. Over the outer section, 5000 feet long, the breakwater runs into the southwest ocean swells. Here, the water is much deeper and wave heights may approach 20 feet. Over 10,000 tetrapods weighing from 9 to 28 tons make up the armoring on this section. At the end, the head is protected by concrete blocks weighing 120 tons. It serves as the anchor for the breakwater, whose outer end has a base width of 260 feet.

The core contains $1\frac{1}{2}$ million cubic yards of rock graded from 20 pounds to 2 tons in weight. Most of this material was carried by dump trucks from a quarry 11 miles away. The trucks ran along the top of the breakwater as it was formed and dumped their loads over the end into the sea. In this way, the core gradually grew seaward. Riprap armoring and large rocks on the outside of the core had to be heavier and tougher. They came by a specially built railroad from a quarry 45 miles away right to the waterfront. Here, two "stiff leg" derricks☞ with 120-foot booms unloaded the wagons and sorted the rock.

The new breakwater, flanked by tetrapods, at Rota Harbor in the Bay of Cadiz.

Next, dump trucks took it on to the breakwater. A hammerhead crane☞ rig weighing 400 tons ran along the top of the breakwater, following the core material as it moved out to sea. This rig placed the big rocks and tetrapods to form the armoring at distances up to 125 feet out from the center line of the breakwater. It took only 3 minutes to pick a 28-ton tetrapod up, swing it round over the water, and set it down. The 120-ton concrete blocks at the head were cast on shore and loaded on barges by a big gantry☞ crane. The barges were then towed out to a floating derrick that set the blocks into position.

Valparaiso has probably the most exposed harbor in the world. It has been described as "a gauntlet flung in the face of nature." The bay is open to the Pacific Ocean and looks impossible as the site for a harbor. Heavy swells and rough seas never cease. In winter, violent storms spring up suddenly. The waves have an enormously long "fetch" from the

Using a working scale model to test a design for a harbor.

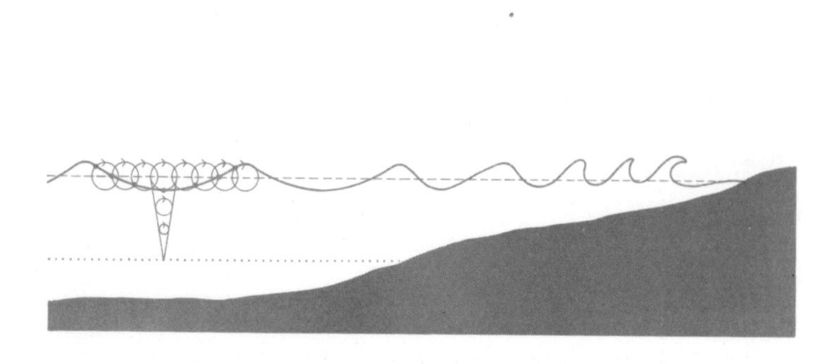

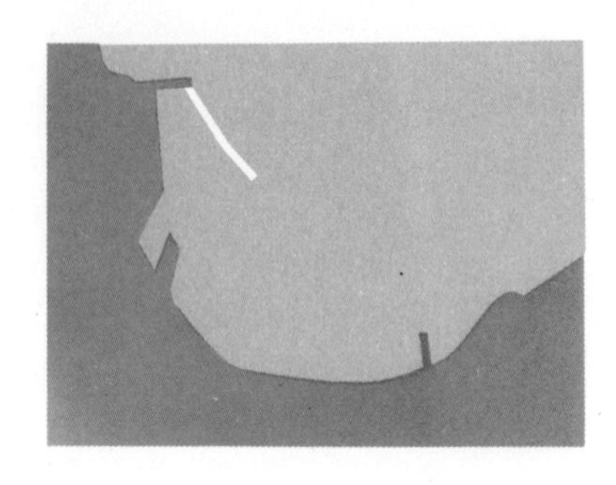

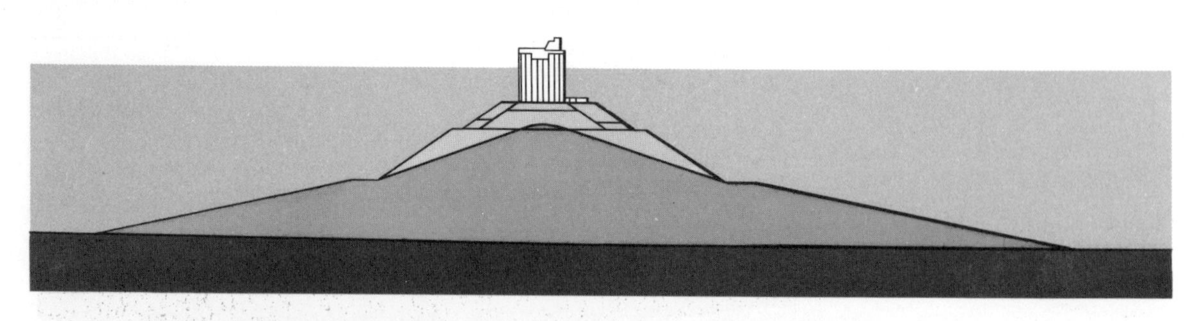

Study of waves in test tanks (upper left) helps in design of breakwaters: Valparaiso's (upper right) was safely built on a sandbank (section, lower).

northwest, and they come at 30 miles an hour, 30 feet high or more. Close to the shore, the water is 100 to 150 feet deep. The sea bottom is of soft mud and fine sand. Moreover, earthquakes often strike the area.

The breakwater protects the harbor from the northerly and northwest seas. It runs from the shore eastward for 1000 feet, then turns sharply to the southeast for about half a mile. Its vertical concrete walls are set on a rock mound dumped on the seabed. For the deeper parts of the eastern breakwater, the rock mound was dumped under the water by hopper barges. Concrete *monoliths* were sunk on top. These are hollow concrete boxes 66 feet long, 53 feet wide, and 50 feet high. They were made in a dock nearby, then floated out and sunk into position. Finally they were filled with concrete so that their 12,000-ton weight would resist the battering of the waves. A number of such monoliths sunk side by side formed a continuous breakwater.

The half-mile long southeast breakwater is in water up to 200 feet deep. Dumping rock mounds on such a deep sea bottom would have been too slow and costly; besides, their weight would have been too heavy for the soft mud seabed. The engineers therefore decided that they would have to raise the seabed itself.

They formed a huge underwater sandbank half a mile long, 1600 feet wide, and over 100 feet high. Two suction dredgers☞ excavated 8,000,000 cubic yards of suitable sand a few miles away and dumped it under water through bottom-emptying hopper barges.

On this huge underwater bank, the barges next dumped quarried rock to form the foundation☞ 40 feet below water level. Finally, engineers built a concrete block wall 53 feet high and 46 feet thick to take the main impact of the waves. These blocks weighed from 45 to 60 tons; they were brought out from the casting yard by barges and picked up and placed by a rig traveling on top of the wall as it grew forward.

Valparaiso harbor, once of evil repute among sailors, still stands after more than 30 years of pounding by the Pacific waves. Some people doubted whether the underwater sandbank would stand up to wave attack. But on the Chilean coast, wave action does not go deeper than 40 feet; the engineers had made sure of this before they began to build.

The breakwater and docks of Salaverry Harbor, on the coast of Peru.

8 Canals Link Land and Sea

For several centuries men sought a Northwest passage to the rich and glamorous East, but never found it. Today when they want a passage between the oceans, they call upon the civil engineer to make one. Great canals☞ bring ships into the very heart of the land. The Suez Canal, linking the Mediterranean to the Red Sea, conducts them through an arid desert wasteland for 100 miles. The Panama Canal, linking the Atlantic and Pacific oceans, carries them across the backbone of the American continent for 50 miles, through a torrid pestilential jungle. The Manchester Ship Canal, 35 miles long, leads them into one of the most densely populated and highly industrialized areas in the world.

In the 16th century, some little time after the boldest of his captains first explored the Panamanian isthmus and beheld the Pacific, Philip II of Spain decreed that no further routes be made across the isthmus, for "God has shown his will in keeping the two oceans apart." In the course of subsequent history however, men were to dream up many schemes for linking Atlantic and Pacific.

When the Panama Canal was built, great though the civil engineer's achievement was, the triumph of the doctors who conquered "yellow jack," malaria, and typhoid was still greater. These diseases had killed an army of workers on the earlier railroad, and in the first disastrous attempt to build the canal. The great De Lesseps, flushed with success at Suez, started the Panama Canal and had to admit defeat after digging 78 million cubic yards and losing 50,000 lives in the fever-ridden jungles.

Some 50 million cubic yards of this total came from the notorious Culebra Cut; this moving mountain, unlike any known before or since, had slid in on the workers as fast as they dug it out. The American army engineers who followed, and completed the canal after 10 years' toil, dug another 230 million cubic yards—100 million from this cut. The first ship went through from sea to sea in 1914, but in 1916 Culebra slid into the canal, blocking it for many months. In 1954, a crack 600 feet deep

Cutting the canal—completed in 1893—through the Isthmus of Corinth.

developed in the mountain, and once again Culebra was on the move. Millions of cubic yards more had to be dug out to make the canal safe. There for the time being Culebra rests.

By far the greatest of all canals is the St. Lawrence Seaway, which runs 2300 miles inland from the Atlantic Ocean into the busy heart of North America. Sixty years of discussion preceded the final decision to go ahead with the canal; then in four and a half years the engineers built this billion-dollar seaway and its hydroelectric power☞ stations. Through the former hunting grounds of the Ojibway and the Algonquin, where the Iroquis and the Huron once paddled their war canoes, the St. Lawrence Seaway now carries ships from many countries.

The main project was a deep seaway running between Montreal and Lake Erie and then on to lakes Huron and Superior. Contending with treacherous rapids, the subzero temperatures of the Canadian winter, high winds, snow storms, ice jams, and fog, the engineers battled on with this

The St. Lawrence Seaway: squares mark the sites of the main locks.

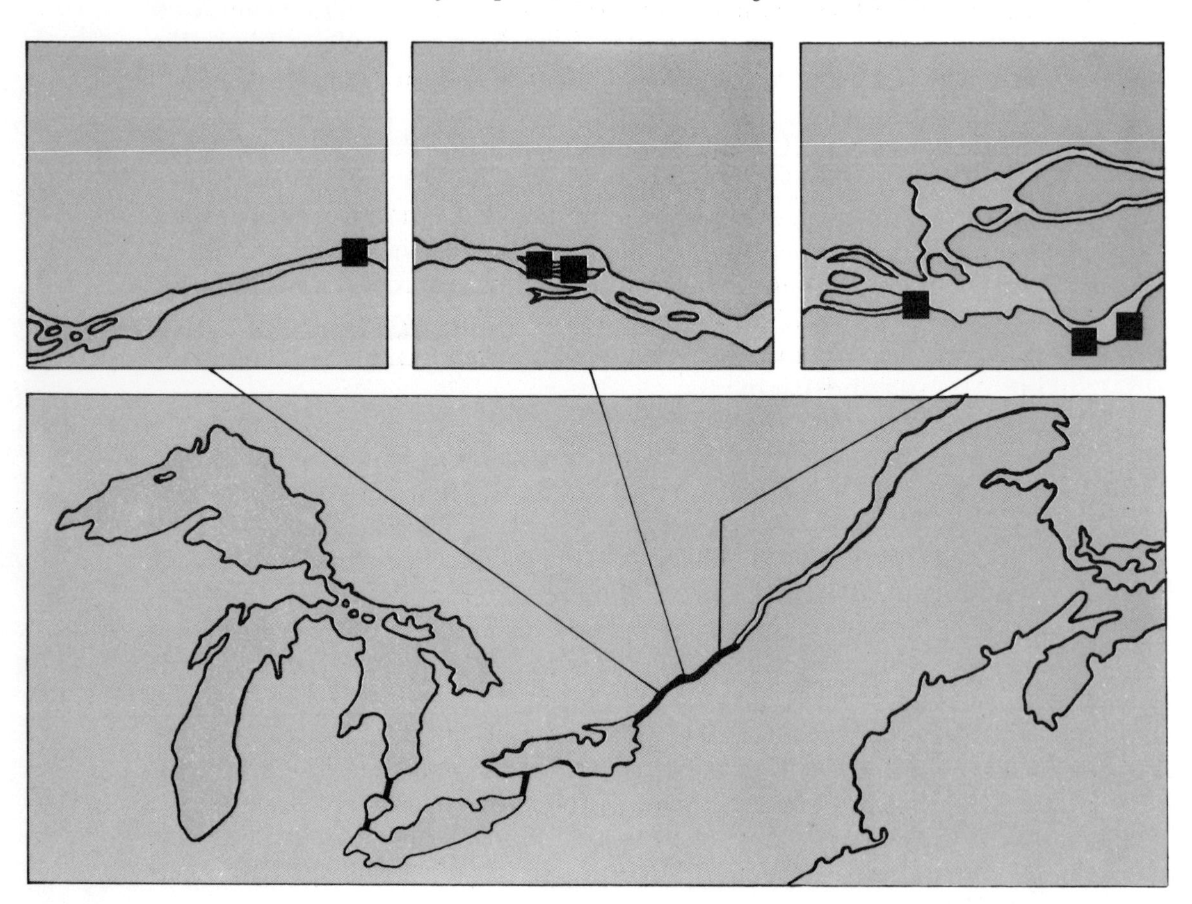

job. And, as though to strengthen the old superstition, the highest river floods for 80 years made their work even more difficult and dangerous.

The St. Lawrence Seaway is a veritable encyclopedia of civil engineering☞, and has already become a landmark in engineering history. But the most astonishing thing of all is the speed at which engineers built it. They excavated 57 million cubic yards of channel to connect the Great Lakes and to bypass the many dangerous rapids. They dredged 20 million cubic yards from the St. Lawrence River and the Great Lakes, deepening them and reshaping them to take large ocean-going ships. They built parts of the seaway in the St. Lawrence itself by throwing up great dikes☞ in the river and digging the seaway out between them.

They built seven great locks☞ as part of the system to raise ships 600 feet on their journey between the Atlantic and Lake Superior. They built two great power dams☞ and a control dam☞ as well as a 38,000-acre power pool, which now provide $2\frac{1}{4}$ million horsepower of hydro-electric energy. They poured some 5 million cubic yards of concrete at fantastic speeds. They built some of the largest cofferdams☞ ever, through the Long Sault Rapids and elsewhere. With brains and determination they overcame the perilous waters and ice jams, and many other difficulties. When they encountered the notorious Potsdam Sandstone rock, which grinds away drill bits in a few minutes, they set up a "jet piercing" rig. This works like a rocket jet, producing a flame, at a temperature of about 2204°C, that burns out the blast holes by vaporizing the rock.

Employing Iroquois who, by a strange twist of fate, are now expert steel erectors and riggers, they built many girder☞ bridges, suspension bridges☞, swing bridges, and lift bridges. They picked old bridges up 50 feet, and they took old bridge spans☞ out and replaced them with new ones, without stopping the flow of traffic.

They moved whole villages, and towns: 200-ton lift rigs picked houses up, carried them to new locations, and set them down on new foundations☞, without disturbing the breakfast cups on the tables. They used giant 165-ton forms 82 feet high, and slip forms☞ that climb up the structure as it is being concreted. They conveyed concrete by pumps, trucks, belts, and cranes.

They used every kind of machine and rig, every suitable technique they could find. The project was so huge, the pace so fast, that they employed more than 20,000 men at the peak of operations. In the spring of 1959, the seaway was ready, and a procession of 78 ships followed the Canadian icebreaker *d'Iberville* into the new St. Lawrence Seaway. Perhaps from their new hunting grounds, the departed spirits of the red men compared this great fleet with Jacques Cartier's tiny ship, when, 400 years ago, he ventured into the unknown and was stopped by the Lachine Rapids near Montreal.

9 Dams Harness Power

The ancient Greek, Antipater, in about 200 B.C., made a list of the seven wonders of the world. Were he alive today, he surely would include one of our modern dams, for they are among the greatest achievements of the civil engineer.

Dams bar the flow of great rivers, raising the level hundreds of feet, diverting the water across the watershed through tunnels, guiding it through turbines that produce a million horsepower, forcing it through great steel pipelines and gigantic gates, enticing it over spillways☞ to fall hundreds of feet, and leading it into placid irrigation canals☞.

Great in the scale of human works, the dam rules remote and sovereign in mountain valleys. It withstands enormous forces, far greater than those resisted by most other structures. No other work of man molds nature so extensively, nor yields such benefits for him. No other work, if it fails, brings such devastation. The dam builder must bring to the task all the resources of his art and science. Every civil engineer who has not built a dam longs to build one; if he has, he longs to build another.

Rivers can be fickle and dangerous. At one time, they may flow gently; at another, they may rise in flood, destroying everything before them and leaving havoc in their wake. The civil engineer must handle them in all their moods. He must divert and contain them, and drain them dry so that he may build great dams rising from foundations☞ deep below the riverbeds. When the dams are built, he turns the rivers back into their old courses, letting the waters rise and pile up against the great walls.

Dam construction has made great progress in the last 50 years. In concrete☞ work, the thick gravity dams☞ of yesterday are giving way to slender arch and double curved arch or "dome" dams☞, and to multiple arch dams. Soil mechanics now makes possible more accurate design for earth-fill☞ and rock-fill dams: these are now built larger and higher than engineers until quite recently thought feasible.

Hoover Dam on the Colorado River—a concrete gravity-arch dam 726 feet high.

Constructing one of the water tunnels of the New High Aswan Dam, Egypt.

A gravity dam relies on its sheer weight to resist the pressure of the water behind it, and is, therefore, very massive. Earth- and rock-fill dams are of this kind. Unlike concrete dams, they need a special impervious core to make them watertight.

An arch dam acts not only by its weight but also by transmitting the water pressure into a thrust against the abutments☞ at either end. In a multiple-arch dam, which has several arches, the thrust is passed to the foundations through a series of heavy piers☞ or buttresses☞. A dam stands in grave danger if the water in the reservoir seeps through the ground under it; the foundation must be made watertight as well as strong. All fissures are therefore sealed by cement injected through holes bored deep into the ground under the dam, thus forming a grout☞ curtain. Before the engineer can begin building a dam, the designer must study the rainfall, and its effects on the main river and its tributaries for many miles upstream: normal and flood time flow must be gauged over a period of years if possible. He then begins designing the dam, while the construction engineer plans his scheme for diverting the river. If, as often, it is too costly to make allowances for abnormal floods, the engineer takes the calculated risk of being flooded out.

But sometimes nature defies all calculations. Construction men insist that the worst floods always occur when they are building a dam. Be that as it may, twice in two years, when engineers were building the Kariba Dam across the great Zambezi in Rhodesia, the river ran at high flood. This concrete arch dam, completed in 1960, now stands 420 feet high. The reservoir forming behind the dam will be the biggest man-made lake in the world: it will hold 149 million acre-feet of water. When work began in 1955, the native witch doctors foretold disaster. "The

The concrete arch of the Kariba Dam across the Zambezi River, Rhodesia.

Spirits of the Zambezi," they declared, "will never allow the white man to invade their kingdom. The dam will never be built."

In March 1957, the Zambezi began to rise. Anxiously the engineers watched the water gauges. With concern they reexamined the flood records, which went back 51 years. The Zambezi continued to rise. Soon it had risen higher than anything their records showed, until some 7000 million gallons of water an hour poured over the cofferdam☞ and flooded out the works. The engineers knew that such a flood might occur, but had decided that a higher cofferdam would take too much time and money. The flood warning system from many miles upstream gave enough time to move most of the machines to safety. The flood subsided quickly; engineers cleaned up the site and resumed work. If any of them thought of the witch doctors' prophecy, they soon dismissed it and got on with the job.

Snowy Mountains scheme (Australia): right, generators in Murray 1 power station; below, Tumut Pond Dam.

The Furnas scheme on the Rio Grande, Brazil: upper, the rock-fill dam, with a height of 400 feet; lower, building the foundations of the powerhouse.

Twelve months later, in March 1958, the Zambezi rose again. This time a freak flood of 13,000 million gallons an hour, about three times the average flow of Niagara Falls, came roaring down the river, causing a million dollars worth of damage. And, perhaps, some of the engineers began to think of the strange tales about native peoples and their miraculous powers of foresight. "The dam will never be built," the witch doctors had said. But it was built. The damage done by the great flood was soon repaired, and in spite of the two setbacks, the dam was finished on time.

The tallest dam now existing is the Grand Dixence in Switzerland. Completed in 1961, it is 932 feet high. The tallest gravity dam is the great Hoover Dam in America, 726 feet high, 660 feet thick at the base, 45 feet thick at the top and containing 3¾ million cubic yards of concrete. Exceeding it by far in volume, although only half the height, is the gigantic Oahe Dam on the Missouri River in South Dakota. This dam

The Bagnes Valley, Switzerland, the site of the Mauvoisin power station. In the mountains above it stands the 777-foot-high Mauvoisin Dam (at left).

is 9300 feet long and contains 90 million cubic yards of earthfill. Through the west bank of the river run six flood-control tunnels, and through the east bank seven power tunnels 24 feet in diameter, feeding water to the turbines☞, which will produce 800,000 horsepower. Other works linked with the dam and powerhouse contain no less than 1 million cubic yards of concrete. The reservoir created by this dam is 200 miles long. A great fleet of mechanical shovels, dump trucks, bulldozers☞, graders☞, rollers, and many other machines excavated, hauled, dumped, spread, and compacted the fill at up to 500,000 cubic yards per week. Modern earth-moving machinery turned this huge undertaking into just another routine job—only bigger.

In recent years, more and more dams are being built everywhere. In highly developed countries, there will soon be no rivers left to dam. But in untouched regions, much can still be done. In some of the great mountain chains where rivers still run their ancient, undisturbed courses, there remains more power than has yet been harnessed.

Some day the world's most powerful single hydroelectric plant may be built on the Tsangpo bend in eastern Tibet. There, the Himalayas tower to fantastic heights, and the river Tsangpo, fed by great glaciers, runs its furious course. After a 1000-mile journey, the river takes a great bend around the 25,500-foot-high peak of Namche Barwa. Here, it breaks into a series of deep gorges and falls over 7000 feet—an enormous concentration of water power. By building a dam where the great bend begins, and driving a tunnel 10 miles long across it under the mountains, the great flow falling through a 7000-foot head could be made to drive turbines. These would produce some 40 million horsepower, which is roughly the equivalent of today's *world total* of hydroelectric power production! But this fantastic source of power is as yet still untapped.

Power dam on the River Volga at Volgograd, USSR.

Tower crane on a building site.

Glossary

In this Glossary, as in the rest of the book, the symbol☞ means that the term it follows has its own alphabetical entry in the Glossary, to which you may refer for a fuller definition or for more information.

ABUTMENT A thick upright support, usually for arches and bridges.

AGGREGATE Loose, heavy material such as gravel, crushed rock, or sand—used in the making of concrete☞, road surfaces, etc.

ALLOY STEEL Steel that has been improved and strengthened, during its preparation, by the addition of other elements—including chromium, manganese, molybdenum.

ANCHORAGE A solidly fixed (usually buried) plate or block that provides an immovable base for one end of a cable, rod, bar, or other structural member☞.

AQUEDUCT A conduit for carrying a large amount of flowing water over distances. The term is most often used for water-carrying bridges.

Aqueduct of 1805.

ARCH BRIDGE A bridge using the arch, or curved beam, as its basic load-bearing element. The simplest arch bridge is the small hump-backed type over narrow streams, on country roads, where the roadway follows the arch itself. On larger versions, the arch acts as a support for a flat deck☞.

ARCH DAM A dam built like an arch laid on its side. It curves into the water, so that the water pressure is transmitted sideways to the abutments☞. A multiple-arch dam is made up of several arches, supported by a series of heavy buttresses☞.

Multiple-arch dam, L. Fedaia, Italy.

ASPHALT Black, tar-like material, produced naturally (by normal decomposition of petroleum deposits) or artificially (during the process of refining petroleum). It is used for roofing, road-surfacing, etc.

BAILEY BRIDGE A flat bridge made from steel lattice☞ girders with a deck☞ of prefabricated steel panels—designed for lightness and for speed of construction.

BARRAGE Any low dam across a river that is intended to raise the water level.

Breakwater, Villefranche, France.

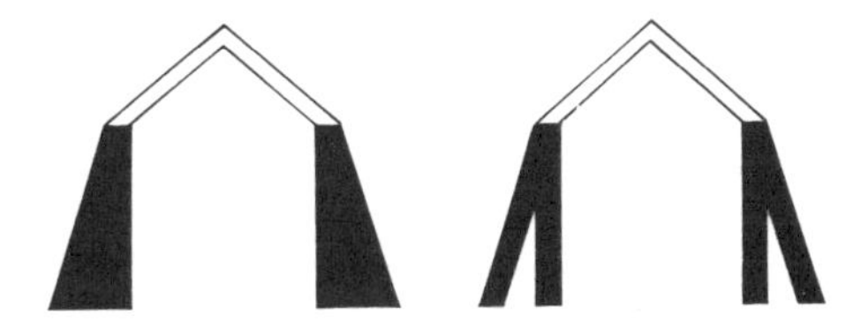

Solid buttress, flying buttress.

Using a caisson to complete a dam.

BEARING WALLS Those walls in a structure that support a load. See also CURTAIN WALLS.

BENT A framework consisting of two uprights joined at the top by a crossbar. Trestle frameworks are usually made of several connected bents.

BONDING Also "adhesion": joining structural members☞ by sticking them together.

BORE Also "borehole": a hole drilled into the ground to investigate the layers of earth below the surface, to release water pressure, or to penetrate a deposit of oil, gas, etc.

BRACE A beam or girder or other member☞, usually placed at an angle to some part of an upright structure as a support.

BREAKWATER A wall built out into the sea to protect the harbor by breaking the force of the waves.

BULLDOZER An earth-moving machine designed mostly for pushing heavy loads of earth. It is mounted on caterpillar tracks, and has a heavy blade ("moldboard") that can be raised or lowered.

BUTTRESS A thick, heavy, upright column☞ built against a wall to strengthen it against a more or less horizontal force. A flying buttress is curved or bowed so that it is not in contact with the wall for its full length.

CAISSON A watertight, open-ended chamber within which it is possible to dig down to solid ground (as for bridge supports) beneath a river, or on a seabed. Caissons are usually left to form part of the support or foundation of the finished structure.

CANAL A channel cut through land and containing water for transport or irrigation☞.

CANTILEVER A beam anchored or weighted heavily at one end, so that the other, unsupported, end can act as a support for parts of a structure.

CANTILEVER BRIDGE A bridge in which two solidly anchored cantilever arms reach out from the sides of the space to be bridged, and support with their free ends the center span☞ of the bridge.

CAST IN SITU Concrete☞ (sometimes plaster) poured while wet into its place in a structure; as opposed to precast concrete☞.

CAUSEWAY A road built on an earth bank or wall over water or marshy ground.

CENTER OF GRAVITY The point at which a body will balance, if supported there.

CIVIL ENGINEERING That branch of engineering which, at its broadest, contains all forms of construction—buildings, railroads, bridges, tunnels, dams, roads, airports and so on—as well as work involved with canals, drainage, harbors, water supply and power, and municipal services.

COFFERDAM A temporary dam, able to be erected quickly, usually consisting of earth or rock or sheet piles☞ driven into the ground across the waterway.

COLUMN Also "long column": a vertical, load-bearing support in a structure. The term now refers mostly to concrete supports; see also STANCHION.

COMPACTION Increasing the density of a substance by packing it down. Heavy road rollers☞ are used for compacting road surfaces.

CONCRETE A mixture of water and sand (or crushed rock) and a binding material such as Portland cement☞. The mixture can be shaped in various ways when wet, then hardens to become stone-like. See REINFORCED, PRECAST, and PRESTRESSED CONCRETE.

CONTROL DAM A temporary dam built to raise the water level, or more often, to give an accurate indication of the water's rate of flow.

CRANE At its simplest, it is a machine with a movable arm (jib☞) from which hangs a cable with a hook or bucket attached. Objects on the

Casting a concrete building in situ.

Cofferdam under construction.

Control dam, St. Lawrence Seaway.

hook or in the bucket can be lifted by the cable (running on a pulley at the end of the jib) and at the same time can be moved horizontally by the turning jib. A gantry or portal crane stands on a framework that runs on rails; a titan crane is a portal crane capable of lifting up to 50 tons. Many other variations exist, some of them self-propelled, some needing manual propulsion. See also DERRICK.

Grabbing cranes on movable gantry.

CRIB DAM A dam built of long timbers or precast concrete☞ beams, stacked flat across each other in an interlocking manner ("cribbing"). The spaces between the beams are filled with earth or rock.

CURTAIN WALLS Walls that enclose a structure but do not bear any of its weight. See also BEARING WALLS.

CUT-AND-COVER A method of digging a tunnel, by cutting a huge open trench, and then covering it over after the tunnel lining has been placed in position inside the trench.

CUTTING An excavation—like a broad, open trench with sloping sides—for a railroad line, canal, road, etc., running below the level of the surrounding ground.

Oil derrick.

DECK The flat roadway of a bridge. A deck bridge consists mainly of girders spanning the space, with the deck running along the tops of the girders. A double-deck bridge has two such surfaces.

DERRICK A stationary lifting device. An oil derrick is a tower of steel girders connected in a lattice☞ pattern, and lifts vertically. A derrick crane☞ has a fixed vertical mast and a horizontal boom across its top, forming a T-shape. The cables and other lifting apparatus hang from one end of the boom—or from a "crab" that can move back and forth along the length of the boom.

DIKE A thick wall of earth along a river bank as a guard against flooding, or across a seafront to protect low-lying lands from the water. See also POLDER and RECLAMATION.

GAUGE The distance between the rails of a railroad line, measured from the inner faces of the rails.

GIRDER A large, long beam, usually of metal but sometimes of prestressed concrete☞, which can be either solid or latticed☞.

GRAB Also "grab bucket": an excavating machine like a large metal mouth. It is hinged in the middle, with tines or teeth on each side. It is lowered, open, by a crane, and closes on a "mouthful" of earth.

GRADER A vehicle used in road-making to prepare the roadbed. It carries a large steel blade that meets the ground surface at an angle to the direction of the road, and scrapes the surface to level it.

GRADIENT Also "grade": the steepness of a slope, measured in degrees from the horizontal, or in a percentage.

GRAVITY DAM An immensely thick dam that resists water pressure by its weight alone. A gravity-arch dam combines great weight with the strength of an arch dam.

GROUT A semiliquid material composed of equal amounts of sand and cement, used for the joints of masonry and similar purposes. It is often driven, under high pressure, into the fissures of a dam or tunnel wall, to seal the wall against water. A "grout curtain" under a dam is formed by forcing grout into a series of holes drilled in the ground beneath the dam, to prevent water seeping through.

GROYNE Also "jetty": a wall built out from land into the sea or into a river, usually to protect against erosion☞.

GUY WIRES Ropes or cables angling down from the top of some comparatively slender structure (such as a tower or mast) and anchored on the ground to keep the structure upright and stable.

GYRATORY A form of rock-breaker in which an inner cone gyrates in a larger, outer hollow cone.

Steel-girder framework for a building.

Grab.

Groynes.

Building the Severn Bridge *The 3240-foot suspension bridge over the River Severn between England and Wales marks two new developments in bridge design: light-weight towers, and a road deck in the form of a hollow box. Stiffened welded steel plates were used to build the towers (upper left); then the main suspension cables were laid (upper right). Sections for the box deck were hoisted into place (center right); and expansion joints were laid in the roadway (lower left) to allow for movement. The finished structure (lower right) is the most economical long suspension bridge yet built.*

HARDCORE Fill☞ composed of hard substances such as broken rock or bricks, broken lumps of concrete, cinders, etc.

HEADING Any small tunnel, but most often a pilot tunnel driven on the proposed route of a large tunnel.

HOLLOW DAM A dam consisting of a single wall—stone or concrete—braced by a series of regularly spaced buttresses☞.

HOT SPRAYING The spraying of paint and lacquer that have been heated to reduce their viscosity (instead of adding volatile thinners). In this way a thicker coat can be formed.

HYDRAULICS The study of the flow and action of liquids—especially water.

HYDROELECTRIC POWER Electricity generated by action of falling water, which turns turbines☞ that drive generators. The water power can be increased by a dam that builds up water pressure and creates a fall.

HYDROGRAPHY Mapping and surveying☞ water courses and flowing water generally.

I-BEAM A steel joist☞ that, when viewed from the end, looks like a capital I.

INERTIA In mechanics, the tendency of a mass to remain at rest or, if in motion, to continue traveling in a straight line unless acted upon by an outside force. In structural work, inertia is a beam's resistance to bending.

IRRIGATION The distribution of water through otherwise dry farmland, by a system of dams, canals, and so on.

JACK Apparatus that lifts heavy loads from underneath. Small jacks (as in motor cars) operate by means of a screw. Larger hydraulic jacks use oil or water pressure.

JIB Also "boom": the lifting arm of a crane☞, angling upward from the base, with a pulley at the upper end over which the lifting cable runs.

Rotor of power-station turbine.

Using a hydraulic jack.

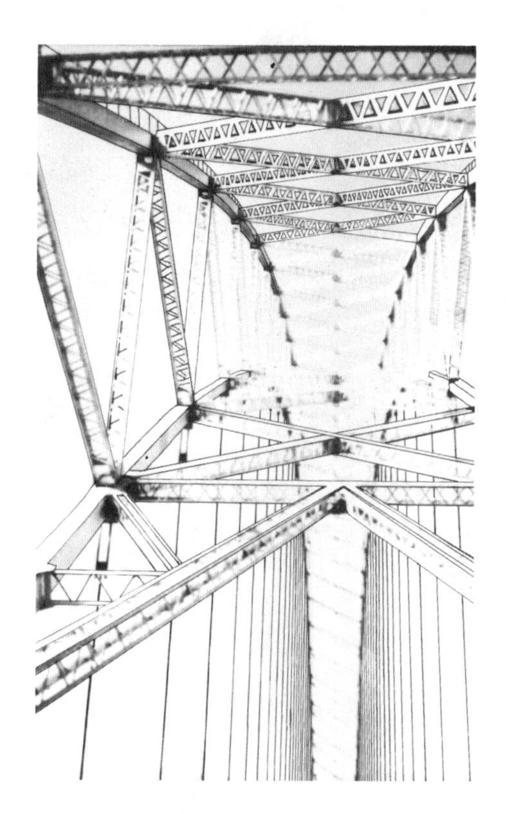

Lattice girders in a steel bridge.

JOIST A beam—of wood, steel, or precast concrete☞. The term is often applied only to beams that support floors of buildings.

LATTICE A term describing crisscrossed bars. In a lattice girder☞ the flat ribbons of metal forming the top and bottom of the girder are joined by welded steel bars in a crisscross pattern like a series of X's.

LEVEL An engineer's instrument that contains a telescope and a "bubble tube" (like a carpenter's level). Used for measuring differences in height of land over considerable distances.

LIFT-SLAB CONSTRUCTION A technique of building in which slabs of concrete for the separate floors of the building (and the roof) are poured one on top of another at ground level and then raised—by jacks☞—onto the supports that have been separately erected.

LITTORAL DRIFT The movement of material such as sand, stones, etc., along a coastline, caused by the action of the sea.

LOCK A section of a canal or other waterway separated by gates from the main stream. The gates can be closed to allow the water level within the lock to be raised or lowered, so that boats may pass to or from the upper reaches of the canal. In this way the canal's water—and the boats on it—can literally travel uphill.

MACADAM Small stones of a uniform size embedded in cement, or coated with tar, and rolled flat to form a hard, impermeable road surface. See TARMACADAM.

MALLEABILITY A metal's ability to be bent or hammered without breaking—so that it can be especially shaped.

MEMBER A term used for any individual element or component of a structure—a wall, beam, column☞, girder☞, etc.

MONOLITH An immense, hollow, open-ended box made of concrete or stone, and used as an open caisson☞.

Locks on the Rideau Canal, Ottawa.

OVERFALL The part of a dam through which water is allowed to pour—or, sometimes, the water itself that pours through the opening. See SPILLWAY.

PAVER A road-making machine that mixes and pours the surfacing material—usually concrete—along the roadway.

Paver, spreader, and finisher.

PERCUSSIVE BORING Sinking a borehole by repeatedly dropping on the same spot a heavy tool that pulverizes, then penetrates, the earth.

PIER Another term for a quay, or for a groyne☞ used as a quay—but also a term for a thick column or short wall of masonry or concrete carrying a heavy weight, as with a bridge support.

PILE Also "piling": a large post of timber, steel, or concrete thrust into the ground (into a prepared hole, or more often by being driven in) to support weight or to form a wall retaining earth or water. A bridge resting on pilings is a "pile bridge." See also FOUNDATION.

PILE DRIVER A machine that lifts the piling into position and also incorporates the pile hammer that drives it into the ground. The hammer, a knob of cast iron or steel, may work by steam power or by gravity—i.e. by being raised mechanically and then allowed to fall onto the piling.

Pile in position on frame.

PIN JOINT A means of joining two members☞ in a structure to permit very slight movement of the members—mostly rotary—so as to offset any tendency to bend. A join by means of a rivet☞ is often a pin joint.

PLANT General term for all the apparatus—including buildings, machinery, scaffolding, etc.—gathered together for an engineering project. The term is also applied to industrial machinery in general.

PNEUMATIC DRILL A powerful rock-breaking implement, in which compressed air drives a sharp metal drill-head in successive bursts against the rock or concrete surface.

Dams and their uses

The Karaj gravity dam (upper), high in the Iranian mountains, stores water for irrigation and provides power for the city of Teheran. The Grand Coulee (center), a straight gravity dam, controls the Columbia River, waters once-deserted farmland, and provides power for the Pacific Northwest. A more specialized structure is the new power barrage at the mouth of the River Rance, Brittany (lower). Here, rising and falling tides are used to drive underwater turbines (sited below sluice gates, at left).

POLDER Land that has been reclaimed from the sea by the erection of dikes☞, or from a swampy, waterlogged state by means of drainage☞.

POND A reach or level stretch of water that lies between canal locks.

PONTOON BRIDGE A bridge supported on flat-bottomed boats or floating rafts of various materials. The pontoons are moored to the riverbed.

Pontoon bridge.

PORT An opening, usually valve-controlled, by which a fluid enters or leaves the cylinder of an engine pump.

PORTAL Also "adit": the entrance to a tunnel.

PORTLAND CEMENT The most widely used form of building cement—a powdery substance that, when mixed with water, hardens into a stone-like mass. (See CONCRETE, also BONDING). It is made by grinding and burning limestone with other materials such as clay or shale.

POWER DAM A dam that controls water to form the driving force in a hydroelectric power☞ station.

PRECAST CONCRETE Concrete poured and hardened into a required shape (for beams, columns☞, piles☞, sections of walls, etc.), before being placed in position in a structure; as opposed to cast in situ☞.

PREFABRICATION The making of various parts and members☞ of a structure separately (and usually in a factory), so they can be quickly and easily assembled on the site of the structure.

Building with prefabricated parts.

PRESTRESSED CONCRETE Concrete that has been strengthened, and made less likely to crack, by having steel bars or wires embedded within it and especially by being compressed. See also REINFORCED CONCRETE.

RECLAMATION The process of restoring land to usefulness (usually for agriculture)—as in the drainage☞ of swamps, the erection of dykes☞ to hold back the sea from lowlands, and so on.

Land reclamation, Holland.

Canal aqueduct with retaining walls.

Sinking a mine shaft (cutaway model).

REINFORCED CONCRETE Concrete given additional strength by having thin steel rods or mesh embedded within it. See also PRESTRESSED CONCRETE.

RELIEVING ARCH An arch—usually of rectangular bricks—built over and clear of a wooden lintel, or other weak support, to carry the main load.

RETAINING WALL A wall built to hold back earth, as on the sides of a railway cutting☞ or a canal embankment☞.

RIPRAP A layer of rocks deposited on a riverbed, or on the banks of a river, to protect against the scour of erosion☞.

RIVET A nail-like steel rod with a rounded head, driven red-hot into prepared holes to join steel members☞ in a structure. See PIN JOINT.

ROLLER A road-making vehicle, used for compacting the roadbed and the road surface. A "sheepsfoot" roller has many short metal bars jutting out from the drum of the roller.

SCRAPER An earth-moving machine consisting mainly of a large bucket that is dragged along the ground on its side, scraping up the earth.

SHAFT A term for a cylindrical rod that transmits power by its lengthwise rotation. Also a term for a vertical or steeply sloping tunnel, giving access from the surface to underground works.

SHIELD A huge, open-ended cylinder of steel used to drive a circular tunnel. It is thrust forward into the earth by jacks☞, and the earth within it can then be removed safely.

SHUTTERING Another term for formwork☞; also, the part of the formwork in direct contact with the concrete.

SILT Fine, light material (like sand but finer grained) carried by river water and deposited along its bed and especially at its mouth. Because of it, harbors at river mouths often require especially frequent dredging.

SLIP FORMS Formwork☞ for building smooth walls or similar structures of concrete that can be raised steadily up the wall as it grows, allowing for nearly continuous pouring of concrete.

SLUICE A term applied either to a gate that can be raised or lowered to control the flow of water in a man-made channel, or to the channel itself, through which water is allowed to gush rapidly (to wash away silt, etc.) when the gate is up.

SPAN The distance between the supports of a bridge, an arch, a beam, a truss☞, etc.

SPILLWAY The channel of a dam through which water is allowed to overflow. See also OVERFALL.

SPREAD FOOTING An extra widening at the base of a wall or other structure, to spread its weight over as wide an area of ground as possible. Usually of reinforced concrete☞.

SPREADER A road-making machine that spreads the surfacing material evenly over the roadbed. See PAVER.

SPRIG A small nail with little or no head.

STANCHION A vertical, load-bearing support in a structure. The term now refers mostly to steel supports; see COLUMN.

STRAIN In terms of structures, a lengthening or shortening of a member☞ due to some outside force.

STRESS In mechanics, the force impinging on a structural member☞ divided by the area that receives the force. In Britain and the USA, stress is expressed in pounds per square inch.

STRUCTURAL ANALYSIS An estimate, before construction begins, of the loads that will be borne by all the members and components of a structure, and the forces that will affect them. The analysis is incorporated into a structural design, which plans the whole structure so that its elements are organized and proportioned accurately and economically.

Building by a slip-form system.

Sluice gates.

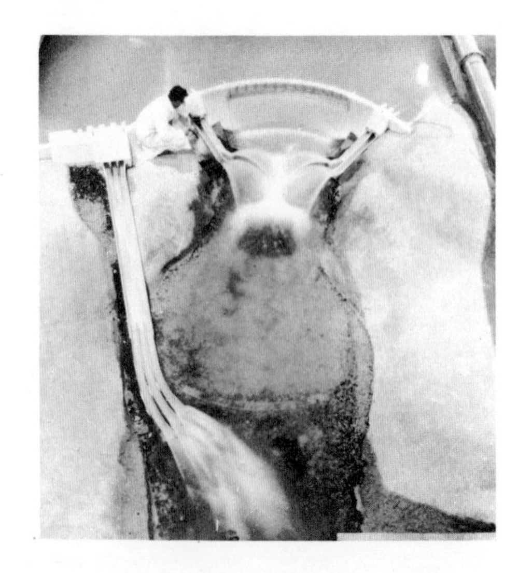

Model for a dam, showing spillways.

On a leveled subgrade a subbase and a base of concrete are laid.

Two layers of asphalt are spread to act as wearing courses.

Chippings are rolled into the asphalt to bind the surface.

STRUT Another term for a column☞ or stanchion☞.

SUBBASE. A layer of material (perhaps fill☞ or hardcore☞) laid on the ground along a proposed roadbed, to strengthen the ground, raise its level, improve its drainage, or for other reasons.

SUBGRADE The ground of a roadbed, on which the subbase☞ and the final surface are laid.

SUBSIDENCE A sinking of the ground, due perhaps to mine tunnels beneath it, or to weakening or other faults in the layers of earth below the surface.

SUMP A pit or pocket in the earth in which water collects, and from which water must be baled or pumped.

SURVEYING The process of examining and mapping an area of land to show the contours of the ground surface, and also to determine the exact position of particular tracts of land (usually with a view to constructing roads, railroad lines, etc. on the tracts).

SUSPENSION BRIDGE A bridge in which the deck☞ is hung from cables stretched across the space and supported by towers on the banks. The cables are fixed in a firm anchorage☞ of rock or masonry, in the ground behind the towers.

SWEAT OUT Plaster that appears damp or mushy after setting. It may be caused by cold weather or by the imperviousness of the backing brick.

TACHOMETER The special telescope in an engineer's theodolite☞, used for exact measurement of distances.

TARMACADAM Material for road surfaces, consisting of small stones coated with tar and compacted. See MACADAM.

TENSILITY Ability of a material to resist stretching. The tensile strength of a metal is an exact measurement of the amount of stretching it can undergo before breaking.

Effects of subsidence on a sea wall.

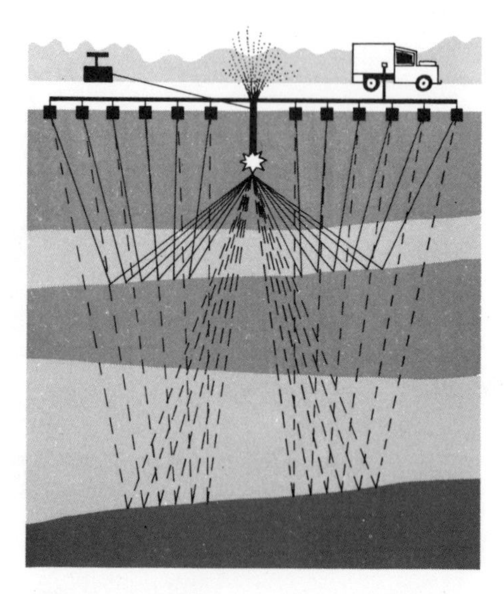

Seismic surveying: an explosion sends shock waves, which can be recorded, into underground rock layers.

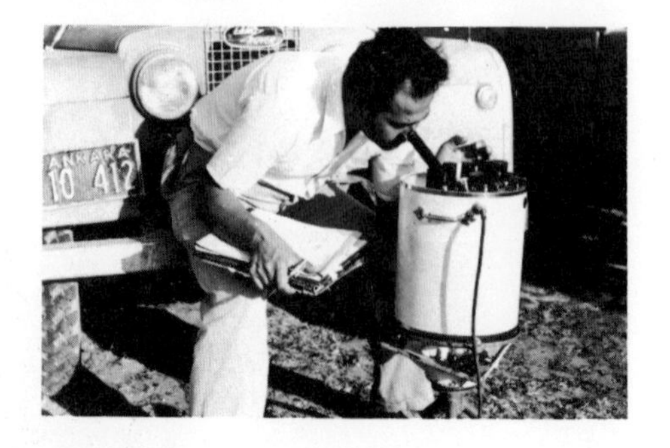

Gravimetric surveying: using a gravimeter to measure variations in the earth's gravitational field.

Tetrapods against a breakwater wall.

Trestle bridge.

Winch in use in a dry dock.

TETRAPOD Big shapes of reinforced concrete☞, with four legs angling out from the central hub—spaced so that the object always rests on three of the legs with the fourth rising vertically. Tetrapods are placed on the seaward side of breakwaters☞ and the like, to resist erosion☞, and to dissipate the force of the waves against the breakwater wall.

THEODOLITE Also "transit": a surveyor's instrument, used mainly for measuring horizontal angles (but sometimes able to measure vertical angles as well). Its principal feature is a telescope (tachometer☞) that rotates horizontally.

THERMAL MOVEMENT Movement due to expansion or contraction caused by temperature change.

THRUST Any horizontal force—most often applied to the force exerted by solid earth on such structures as retaining walls☞.

TORSION Also "torque": a twisting force, like that applied by one's hands when wringing out a cloth.

TRESTLE BRIDGE A bridge supported by a series of connected bents☞, made of timbers, pilings, or steel beams placed upright and thoroughly braced.

TRUSS A rigid framework built up of steel beams interconnected and angled like a series of triangles. Often used as supporting framework of a light bridge.

TURBINE A rotary engine driven (like a sophisticated waterwheel) by the force of flowing water against curved vanes.

VIADUCT A term for a road bridge (sometimes a railroad bridge) whose spans☞ are carried on a series of piers☞ placed fairly close together.

WEIR Another form of control dam☞.

WINCH A lifting device, usually hand-operated, in which a cable (often passing through a system of pulleys) is wound onto a revolving drum.

Index

Page numbers in *italics* refer to illustration captions.

Picture Credits

Endpapers Mansell Collection
2 Aero Service Corporation, Philadelphia
6 Bibliothèque Nationale, Paris/Photo Françoise Foliot
8 Popperfoto
15 Susan Tibbles
16–17 KLM photos
18 Barnabys Picture Library
20 (TL) Editions Cahiers d'Art, Paris
(TR) Camera Press
(BR) Susan Tibbles
21 USIS, London
23 (TL) From *Domus*, No. 348, Pirelli Tower, Milan, designed by Studio Ponti, Fornaroli and Rosselli and Studio Valtolina, Dell'Orto, with the consultantship of Pier Luigi Nervi and Arturo Danusso, 1958
(BL) French Government Tourist Office, London
24 Cement and Concrete Association
25 © *The Times*
26 © Newsweek/Photo Dale Healy
29 Photos Caterpillar Tractor Co. Ltd.
33 Aerofilms Ltd.
34 Triborough Bridge and Tunnel Authority, New York
38–41 United States Information Service, London
42 Picturepoint, London
43 Aerofilms Ltd.
45 Venezuelan Embassy, London
46 United States Travel Service, London
48 Keystone/Publifoto, Milan
51 Aluminium Company of Canada Limited
53 London Transport Board
55 Keystone/Publifoto Milan
56 Photo Collection Chambre de Commerce et d'Industrie de Marseilles/Photo Cellard
59 Société Grenobloise d'Etudes et d'Applications Hydrauliques, Paris
62 Mansell Collection, redrawn by Susan Tibbles

66 Picturepoint, London
68 Camera Press
70 (B) Photo Snowy Mountain Hydro-Electric Authority
72 Swiss National Tourist Office, London
73 Novosti Press Agency
74 Picturepoint, London
76 (T) British Travel Association
(B) Photo L. V. Taylor
77 (T) Photo Jack Scheerboour
(B) Photo Bart Hofmeester
78 (T) Cement and Concrete Association
(B) Ontario Hydro. St. Lawrence Seaway Project
79 (T) Stothert & Pitt Ltd.
(B) A Shell photo
80 (T) Photo Gordon Howard
(C) Barnabys Picture Library
81 (T) Popperfoto
(C) Mansell Collection
(B) Cement and Concrete Association
82 (T) Courtesy British Iron & Steel Federation
(B) Picturepoint, London
83 Joint Consulting Engineers: Freeman Fox & Partners and Mott, Hay & Anderson
84 (T) The English Electric Company Limited
(B) Welch-Simes-Willetts Ltd./ Photo J. R. Poulter
85 (T) Picturepoint, London
(B) Photo J. Allan Cash
86 (T) Laszlo Acs
(B) Photo John Laing & Son Ltd.
87 (T) Syndication International
(C) Aerofilms Ltd.
(B) French Government Tourist Office, London
88 (T) Photo J. Allan Cash
(C) Popperfoto
(B) Rijvsdienst Voor de IJsselmeerpolders Zivolle
89 (B) National Coal Board
90 (T) Cement and Concrete Association
(C) KLM photo
(B) Hydraulics Research Station, Wallingford. British Crown Copyright. Reproduced by permission of the Controller of Her Britannic Majesty's Stationery Office
92 (T) Popperfoto
(B) A Shell photo
93 (T) Neyrpic, Grenoble
(C) Photo J. Allan Cash
(B) Stothert & Pitt Ltd.
Courtesy George Wimpey & Co. Ltd.: 52, 61, 71
Photos J. Allan Cash: 70T, 78C, 80B, 85B, 88T, 93C

Endpapers: an early 18th-century drawing of the two sides of London Bridge.

THE WEST-SIDE O
THE EAST-SIDE O